Santa Clara
County
Free Library

REFERENCE

 58 16

SCIENCE AND CULTURE SERIES
JOSEPH HUSSLEIN, S.J., Ph.D., GENERAL EDITOR

WHEN THE EARTH QUAKES

WHEN THE EARTH QUAKES

By

JAMES B. MACELWANE, S.J.

THE BRUCE PUBLISHING COMPANY
Milwaukee

PREFACE BY THE GENERAL EDITOR

In some of the most beautiful parts of the world earthquakes are a dreaded scourge. Many a majestic ruin speaks eloquently through its broken arches and its prone-lying columns of the ravages of some giant earthquake in the long ago. And far back beyond all history the geologist reads in the rocks the record of countless fossil earthquakes. The number of earthquakes that occur now in one year is reliably estimated at more than a million. Ours is indeed a quaking earth.

The fear of so terrible a menace, which strikes in the dark when least expected, has driven primitive peoples and even civilized communities into superstitious awe of earthquakes. The author of this book relates that he was once approached by an Italian workman with the query: "Are you studying earthquakes?" On receiving an affirmative answer, the workman's face blanched and he said in a most deprecative tone: "Don't do it! Leave them alone. They are the scourge of God." Commercial interests in some of our western communities have opposed the study of earthquakes for no less mistaken though more material reasons. We may recall that for decades the San Francisco earthquake was only a fire. The Italian workman at least was willing to admit the fact of earthquakes; and he was correct in supposing that these natural phenomena occur by the disposition of God's Providence.

This book brings before the reader in nontechnical language the wealth of knowledge that has been gleaned from the scientific study of earthquakes and of their related phenomena both natural and man-made. The reader sees enacted before his eyes, as it were, the titanic drama of struggle within the earth beneath his feet; the clash of giant forces fashioning anew the "eternal" hills; the shudders that grip our Mother Earth as the rocks of ages in her bosom are wrenched asunder and hurled hither and yon in this gargantuan

v

battle. The astonished reader sees the dark recesses of the earth's inaccessible interior lit up, as it were, by the flash of earthquake energy, revealing to him its structure. He learns how similar forces are harnessed by the mining and petroleum industries to ferret out the hiding places of precious ores and oil. Finally the reader is taught the process of taming these forces for the beneficent task of providing protection for life and property against the menace of earthquakes.

The writer of this volume is qualified to speak authoritatively on his subject. He began the study of seismology at St. Louis University in 1910, and in 1923 he received from the University of California his doctorate in physics with a thesis based on seismological research. From 1921 to 1925 he was in charge of the earthquake stations of the University of California at Berkeley and Mount Hamilton. As assistant professor of geology he taught courses and developed graduate studies in seismology at the University of California in Berkeley between 1923 and 1925. In the latter year he was called back to St. Louis University to organize the first department of geophysics in the Western Hemisphere. From 1927 to 1933 he was dean of the Graduate School of St. Louis University. In 1944 he organized the Institute of Geophysical Technology and is now its dean.

That he has the confidence and esteem of his colleagues is shown by the fact that his research in geophysics is starred in *American Men of Science* as well as by his election to the National Academy of Sciences, and by the positions of honor and trust he has been chosen to fill. He has held the office of president of the Seismological Society of America, of the Section of Seismology of the American Geophysical Union, of the Jesuit Seismological Association, of the Missouri Academy of Science, and of the Academy of Science of St. Louis. He has been chairman of the Section of Geology and Geography and vice-president of the American Association for the Advancement of Science. He was chosen as one of the national lecturers of the Society of the Sigma Xi for the Promotion of Research in Science; and his lecture on the interior of the earth was asked for by thirty-two chapters of that honor society. He is a member of many national boards and committees and has been engaged in war research work.

This now should suffice to introduce the author to those far wider and more popular circles who may be interested in the subject here treated, and in securing reliable information on the scientific study of earthquakes: its nature, methods, and results.

JOSEPH HUSSLEIN, S.J., PH.D.,
General Editor, Science and Culture Series.

St. Louis University,
January 23, 1947.

INTRODUCTION

Before one reads a book on any science he naturally would like to know what is in store for him. The science that treats of earthquaking is called *seismology*. It belongs in the great group of earth sciences known as geophysics. Like the rest of these sciences it lies on the boundary between physics and geology. Its name is pronounced size-mol'-o-jy and it is taken from the Greek, σεισμολογία (*seismologia*), which, in turn, is derived from the Greek word σεισμός (*seismos,* an earthquake). Therefore, etymologically, seismology means the science of earthquakes; but it is much more than that.

Seismology deals not only with earthquakes as they are felt, but with the nature and causes of earthquakes and their relation to other geological processes in the earth, with the kinds of earthquakes, their intensity and distribution, with their effects on land and sea and especially on structures built by man, and with all the problems of engineering that arise from them.

But seismology is even more than that. It includes the physics of earthquake waves propagated through and around the earth and the fascinating story these waves have been made to tell us of the hidden depths of our planet. It treats of man-made earthquakes, the vibrations caused by blasts of explosives, their effects on buildings and other structures, and their use in determining the hidden make-up of the earth's outer shell, thereby assisting us in the location of valuable mineral deposits, and especially of petroleum. Lastly, seismology deals with shaking of the earth's crust even when it has no known connection with earthquakes either natural or artificial.

Seismology therefore, has a manifold aspect. Its outlook is mathematical; its tools and methods are physical; but it utilizes to the full the data of geology and describes its results in the language of that science. Finally, it lends itself readily to the service of applied science in the hands of the architect, the engineer, the insurance expert, and the prospector.

Modern seismology as a branch of geophysics began its existence in the latter half of the nineteenth century and it is still in the full vigor of youthful development. The reader who is interested in the history of the science will find *The Founders of Seismology* by Charles Davison of great assistance.

CONTENTS

CONTENTS

WHEN THE EARTH QUAKES

Chapter I

WHAT EARTHQUAKES DO

A flagello terraemotus, libera,
nos Domine.
"From the scourge of the earthquake,
deliver us, O Lord."
— Litany of All Saints.

Acquaintance With Earthquakes

Before anyone can form a really intelligent opinion concerning the facts and theories of seismological science one must know something about earthquakes as they are seen and felt. This knowledge may be acquired in several ways. One may have lived through a destructive earthquake and have had the courage and the presence of mind to observe what was going on around him, and have had the ability, and the necessary facilities to study scientifically the effects it produced. Such experience falls to the lot of few and would be willingly sought by fewer, even if it were a matter of deliberate choice.

Again, a person may have experienced less violent shocks on the one hand, and on the other he may have gone into a stricken area to make a careful survey of the changes wrought. This is an expensive means of learning, and it presupposes unusual opportunities which are quite beyond the reach of the average person who is interested in seismology. Besides, if one were to undertake field studies without previous acquaintance with the theoretical side of the science of seismology he would be sure to make grave mistakes. He would overlook or misinterpret many of the most significant facts.

For the great majority of people, then, the only trustworthy means of acquiring a knowledge of earthquakes will be the reading of accounts and descriptions written by experts.

1

— Courtesy Nat'l Board of Fire Underwriters

Fig. 1. Jefferson Junior High School, Long Beach. Destroyed in the Long Beach earthquake, March 10, 1933.

Caution Concerning Popular Accounts

Newspaper reports are often unintentionally misleading. They are written by journalists under the stress and excitement of a public calamity. As a general rule the writers have no training in seis-

— Courtesy Nat'l Board of Fire Underwriters

Fig. 1a. Compton Junior High School. Destroyed in the Long Beach earthquake, March 10, 1933.

— Photo by A. C. Lawson

Fig. 2. Houses on Golden Gate Avenue opposite Jefferson Square, San Francisco, whose underpinning failed in the earthquake of April 18, 1906. The steps at No. 821 remained in their original position, while the house was thrown about four feet toward the left, parallel to the street, and was dropped to the ground.

mology. They have neither the time nor the ability to check all of the exaggerated reports that come to them from apparently reliable witnesses. Newspapers and popular magazines want photographs with news appeal. Consequently their illustrations tend to emphasize the unusual, the bizarre, and the sensational rather than the ordinary and the normal. Obviously the photograph of one building that has been razed to the ground is far more effective as earthquake news than would be pictures of the hundred and one other structures that went through the earthquake unscathed. The distortion is not necessarily one of fact but of emphasis. Yet the general public is thereby misled and gains a false impression of the extent of the damage.

How the Quaking Affects Man and Animals

The effects of earthquake motion on human beings are surprisingly varied. In addition to the mental stress induced by fear and a feeling of helplessness in the face of overpowering forces, a person is subjected to unpleasant physiological conditions such as nausea, headache, disturbance of the equilibrating mechanism in the ears and of the fluid in the eyeballs so that the sight is distorted and one sees solid structures, such as walls, towers, and concrete floors waving in a manner that would break them in pieces if these visible waves were real. All this often induces an abnormal psychological

— Photo by A. C. Lawson

Fig. 3. Chimney on the house of Professor A. C. Lawson, 2461 Warring Street, Berkeley, California, thrown diagonally toward the southeast in the earthquake of April 18, 1906.

state so that persons perform actions of which they have not the slightest recollection when the earthquake is over, or suffer hallucinations concerning what they believe they have seen.

Brute animals are affected by earthquake vibrations in an analogous manner. Dogs bark, horses and cattle stampede, fowls be-

— Photo by E. A. Hodgson

Fig. 4. Tombstones at Riviere Ouelle, Quebec, overthrown toward the southeast by the earthquake of
February 28, 1925.

— Photo by R. S. Holway

Fig. 5. Monument at Sebastopol, California, the upper part of which walked on the
lower part and the whole walked on the
ground, without any permanent rotation of
either, in the earthquake of April 18, 1906.

come excited, birds take wing. Even fish have been observed to behave abnormally at the time of an earthquake.

Effects of Slight Earthquakes on Structures

The effects of earthquake motion can be seen to best advantage, of course, in those shocks which are strong enough to cause visible damage.

In slight earthquakes the forces which act leave behind them no visible mark. They betray their presence only by the swaying and rattling, the displacements which they produce for the moment and which immediately cease and disappear with the passing of the shock. Only a motion picture camera could possibly photograph these t r a n s i e n t and continuously changing effects; and such a camera would itself be disturbed and, as a result, its pictures would be distorted by the earthquake.

— Photo by E. A. Hodgson. Courtesy Dominion Observatory, Ottawa, Canada

Fig. 6. Monument at Riviere Ouelle, Quebec, which was rotated clockwise by the earthquake of February 28, 1925. The spalled edges of its pedestal indicate that the upper block rocked violently while rotating.

Primary Effects of Strong Earthquakes

In very strong earthquakes the shaking is so severe that damage usually results. Whether a given structure will fail or will go through the earthquake unharmed depends on many different factors.

First there are the inertia effects of sudden lurches. Every material body, as we know, has a property called inertia, which tends to keep it always in the same state. This property of a material body tends to resist any attempt to start the body moving if it is at rest, or to change its speed or direction if it is in motion. Therefore if the ground gives a sudden lurch in an earthquake all loose objects tend

— Photo by A. C. Lawson. Courtesy Carnegie Inst. of Washington

Fig. 7. The swaying of the steel frames of the steeples of St. Dominic's Church, Bush and Steiner Streets, San Francisco, in the earthquake of April 18, 1906, knocked down the steeple walls. The church stood on alluvium and sand of no great depth.

to be left behind because of their inertia. Thus houses are displaced on their foundations, or they break off their underpinnings and fall. Furniture moves about. Chimneys topple. Water spills. Walls and monuments are overthrown.

More often the ground sways back and forth, lurching first this way then that. Loose objects that are not overthrown by the first lurch may be set rocking on their bases. Furniture may thus "walk"

— Photo by A. C. Lawson. Courtesy U. S. Geol. Survey

Fig. 8. Cracks caused in the plastered wall of a brick house, corner of Fifteenth and Landes Streets, San Francisco, California, by the earthquake of April 18, 1906.

many feet. Monuments rotate because of eccentric friction on their pedestals. Hanging objects swing back and forth through large arcs. Pendulum clocks are stopped. Trees, tall poles, and steeples sway.

When buildings are thus subjected to strong back and forth oscillations their structural parts are sheared and their walls may be overstrained. X-cracks frequently appear in wall panels as a result of such shearing. Floors and even the ground may be sheared horizontally. Diagonal bracing is often pulled out. Tank towers are sheared off and collapse.

Fig. 9. "X" cracks in the wall of St. John's Hospital, Helena, Montana, produced by the earthquakes of 1935.

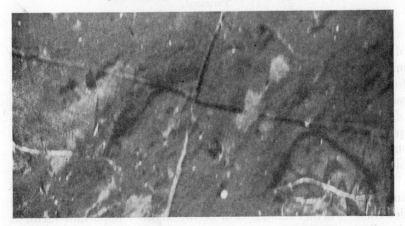

Fig. 10. "X" cracks in frozen ground caused by shearing movement during the earthquake of February 28, 1925, at Sainte-Anne de la Pocatiere, Quebec.

— Courtesy Nat'l Board of Fire Underwriters

Fig. 11. Reinforced concrete column sheared in the earthquake of March 10, 1933. Southwest corner of the tower of the Los Angeles Union Terminal.

In most earthquakes the vertical oscillations are of the same order of magnitude as the horizontal vibrations and the forces involved may, for brief intervals of time, approximate or even surpass the force of gravity. Under such circumstances brick chimneys and masonry walls may be lifted brick by brick and stone by stone clear of the mortar between them and then be dropped back nearly or quite into place when the wave has passed. Many fires have been started after earthquakes through the use of such apparently intact but actually dismembered structures.

However, the magnitude and direction of the earthquake forces and the inertia reactions of structures are not the only factors that determine whether damage will occur. Another important factor is the relation of the tempo of the earthquake shaking to the natural period of the structure. If the two are in step larger movements will

Fig. 12. Tank tower near Los Angeles which
collapsed in the earthquake of March 10, 1933.

Fig. 13. Chimneys at Elsinore, Utah, ruined by earthquakes of
September 29 and October 1, 1921. The bricks of the chimney at left
were lifted and dropped back at an angle of about 45° with their original position. An eyewitness saw the bricks of the chimney at right
lifted and dropped. Two bricks were thrown about sixteen feet.

Fig. 14. Stone house near Riviere Ouelle, Quebec, which had to be taken down and rebuilt because all the stones in the walls had been lifted from one another by the earthquake of February 28, 1925. The house appears intact except for the loss of its chimney and patches of stucco but it really remained only a pile of loose stones.

Fig. 15. Arches of the geology building at Stanford University, California, wrecked by the earthquake of April 18, 1906.

— Photo by H. W. Fairbanks

Fig. 16. Scars of landslides at Chittenden Pass in the canyon of the Pajaro River, California. The narrow streak in the cliff at the right is the trace of the San Andreas fault of April 18, 1906, which crossed the Canyon at this point.

— Photo by R. Anderson. Courtesy Carnegie Inst. of Washington

Fig. 17. Mud flow four miles east of Half Moon Bay, Califorina, caused by the earthquake of April 18, 1906.

— Courtesy California Earthquake Investigation Commission

Fig. 18. Slumping of alluvial ground toward the Salinas River near Spreckels, California, in the earthquake of April 18, 1906.

occur as the shaking continues and the probability of damage is greater than if the two are completely out of step. This condition is called *resonance*.

A closely related cause of destruction is the ramming action of two adjacent buildings or of two parts of the same building which have different natural periods and consequently get out of step and batter each other down when shaken by an earthquake.

Secondary Effects of Earthquakes

Landslides occur at any time under favorable conditions. But an earthquake may furnish just the trigger action that is necessary to start a slide which is not quite ready to go of itself and which otherwise might have stood for a long time. Very many landslides were started by the California earthquake of April 18, 1906. If the material of the slide is composed of solid rock it is called a *rock slide*.

Sometimes the soil on a slight incline has absorbed so much moisture that the shaking of the earthquake is able to start it moving downhill. It may then become extraordinarily mobile and may flow under the influence of the vibrations for considerable distances. Such a phenomenon is called a *mud flow*. Where there is less mobility we

— Photo by Harry O. Wood

Fig. 19. Slump of filled ground on Union Street
west of Steiner Street, San Francisco, California,
caused by the earthquake of April 18, 1906.

— Photo by T. D. LaTouche. Courtesy Survey of India

Fig. 20. Fissure at Rowmari, India, caused by the Assam
earthquake, June 12, 1897.

— Photo by T. Beckwith. Courtesy U. S. Geol. Survey

Fig. 21. Earthquake fissure filled with intruded sand, near Charleston, Missouri.

— Courtesy Jesuit Mission Press

Fig. 22. Sand craterlets formed during the Bihar
earthquake, January 15, 1934.

— Photo by J. C. Branner. Courtesy Carnegie Inst. of Washington

Fig. 23. Sand crater near Watsonville, California, formed during the earthquake of April 18, 1906.

have what is called a *slump*. Filled ground on a slope is especially subject to slumping. Readjustments of level on a large scale occurred during the New Madrid earthquakes of 1811–1812.

Another secondary effect of earthquake motion is extrusion of sand or mud. The alternate tension and compression which is applied to the ground during the passage of earthquake waves opens *fissures* and sucks down the ground water, then closes them, violently forcing out the water and with it large quantities of sand or mud that lay in its path. If the sand and water are forced out through individual vents they will form *craterlets,* or they may form fairly large *sand craters.* If the volume of extruded water is large enough to spread far from the fissures it will give rise to *sand blows* and may completely ruin farm land.

The shaking and shearing motion of an earthquake often produces *ground cracks* even at considerable distances from the center of the disturbance.

The most fearful and destructive of the secondary effects of earthquakes is fire. Broken gas pipes and mains and electrical short-circuits are prolific sources of fires. So too is the lighting of stoves that are connected to damaged chimneys. To make matters worse, the water mains are usually damaged or broken by the earthquake

— Photo by M. L. Fuller. Courtesy U. S. Geol. Survey

Fig. 24. Sand blows in northeastern Arkansas caused by the New Madrid earthquakes of 1811–1812.

so that it is impossible to extinguish the fires that arise. The fires that followed the earthquake in San Francisco in 1906 and in Tokyo September 1, 1923, brought about a greater loss of lives and of property in those cities than did the earthquakes which caused the fires.

In the preceding paragraphs we have seen some of the effects of the shaking in an earthquake. But why does the earth quake? Why

— Photo by M. L. Fuller. Courtesy U. S. Geol. Survey

Fig. 25. Stumps of trees killed by deposits of sand extruded during the New Madrid earthquakes, 1811–1812.

— Courtesy Jesuit Mission Press

**Fig. 26. Cracks in the ground at Muzaffarpur, India,
caused by the Bihar earthquake, January 15, 1934.**

should the solid ground tremble and sway? We shall attempt to
answer these questions in later chapters; but first it will be necessary to know something about our changing earth and the geological
processes that are at work refashioning it; for the sources of earthquake vibrations are to be found in the more permanent ground displacements that constitute as it were the youthful twitchings and
growing pains of our mobile earth. The reader who is not familiar
with geology will find a useful summary in Appendix A.

Fig. 27. Saint Ignatius Church and College at the northwest corner
of Hayes Street and Van Ness Avenue, San Francisco, California,
gutted by the fire which followed the earthquake of April 18, 1906.

Chapter II

SOME MODERN EARTHQUAKES

In order to get a better view of our quaking earth let us examine a few of the earthquakes of history that have been considered important enough to have treatises written about them.

One of the more important ones is the California earthquake[1]* of April 18, 1906.

San Francisco Earthquake

In the early hours of the morning — at eleven minutes and fifty-eight seconds after five o'clock Pacific Standard Time to be exact — the inhabitants of San Francisco and of the other cities of central California were shaken from their beds amidst a roar of dropping

---

* Small numbers in the text refer to corresponding reference numbers in Appendix B.

— Photo by R. S. Holway

Fig. 28. Buildings on Fourth Street, Santa Rosa, California, completely ruined by the earthquake, April 18, 1906.

20

Fig. 29. Looking along Dore Street, San Francisco, from Bryant toward Brannan, after the earthquake of April 18, 1906; showing partially wrecked frame buildings and broken and undulating pavement.

Fig. 31. Rent in the earth's crust formed by faulting in the California earthquake, April 18, 1906. The left side was shifted away from the reader, the right side toward him, the relative displacement approximating eighteen feet. Near Olema, Marin County, California.

plaster, falling masonry and chimneys, breaking chinaware and glass, and tumbling, crashing furniture. The shock increased in intensity, subsided somewhat, and then increased again. In all it lasted more than one minute. A narrow zone of destruction extended

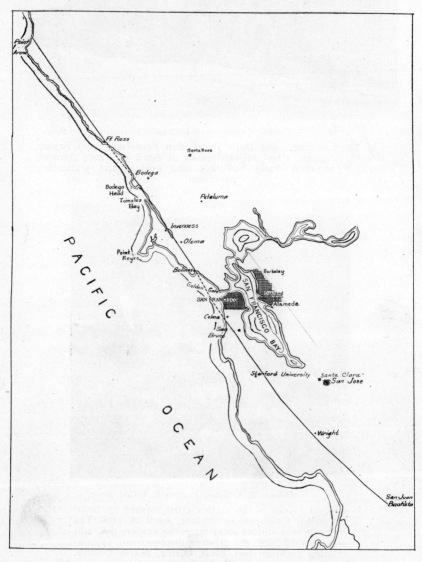

Fig. 30. Map of the California Earthquake, April 18, 1906.

— Photo by R. S. Holway

Fig. 32. Earthquake crack or fault trace of April 18, 1906, crossing the marshy flat at the head of Tomales Bay in the San Andreas Rift. The tract on the left was carried in the direction away from the reader past that on the right, tearing up great blocks of turf.

— Photo by J. N. Leconte. Courtesy Carnegie Inst. of Washington

Fig. 33. Trace of the earthquake fault of the California earthquake of April 18, 1906, a mile and a half north of Fort Ross, where it follows the scarp or cliff of an older fault.

Fig. 34. Slickensided fault plane near north end of
Crystal Springs Lake.

from Humboldt County on the northwest to Monterey County on
the southeast, a distance of more than three hundred miles. The
earthquake was felt over an area comprising all the region between
Coos Bay, Oregon, on the north, Winnemucca, Nevada, on the east,
and Los Angeles on the south, totaling 175,000 square miles inland
from the coast, and probably little short of double that area if we
include that portion of the sea bottom which must have been similarly affected. The earth's crust was visibly rent from Telegraph
Hill, a little south of Petrolia in Humboldt County, to the sea at
Shelter Cove and again from Point Arena in Mendocino County to

— Courtesy California Earthquake Investigation Commission

Fig. 35. Road to Inverness, California, which had been straight before the earthquake of April 18, 1906, offset twenty-one feet where it was crossed by the earthquake fault.

a point in San Benito County near San Juan Bautista, a total distance of 270 miles. This rent is the surface trace of what the geologist calls a *fault* in the rocks below.

When a portion of the earth's crust is so strained as to crack or tear and cause the rocks on one side to slip past those on the other,

— Courtesy Carnegie Inst. of Washington

Fig. 36. The earthquake fault of April 18, 1906, passing in front of Skinner's ranch house, near Olema, California, and carrying the garden walk eighteen feet toward the left.

the plane along which the slip occurs is called a fault. In the California earthquake there may have been two faults *en echelon* instead of one, because the trace was covered by the sea south of Shelter Cove and its prolongation does not line up with the part south of Point Arena. The first of these two faults then, if there are two, appears in the stretch from Telegraph Hill to Shelter Cove; and the second, parallel to the first but farther toward the southwest, extends from Point Arena southeastward. This latter fault follows an old belt of dislocation, a fault zone marked by typical rift features, which are particularly well developed in the San Andrés Valley on the San Francisco Peninsula and which have therefore given to this striking geomorphic feature the name of San Andrés Rift. It is one of the major tectonic or structural lines of California. Its seismic activities go back at least to late Tertiary times. Earthquakes are known historically to have recurred on it; and farther to the southeast it was commonly called "the earthquake crack." Beyond San Juan Bautista the San Andreas Rift traverses a mountainous region, skirts the southwestern edge of the Mojave desert and the northern slope of the San Gabriel Mountains, crosses through Cajon Pass to the southern flank of the San Bernardino Mountains, and is finally lost in the Colorado desert.

— Photo by J. C. Branner. Courtesy Carnegie Inst. of Washington

Fig. 37. Alpine Road, five miles west of Stanford University, offset by the earthquake fault of April 18, 1906.

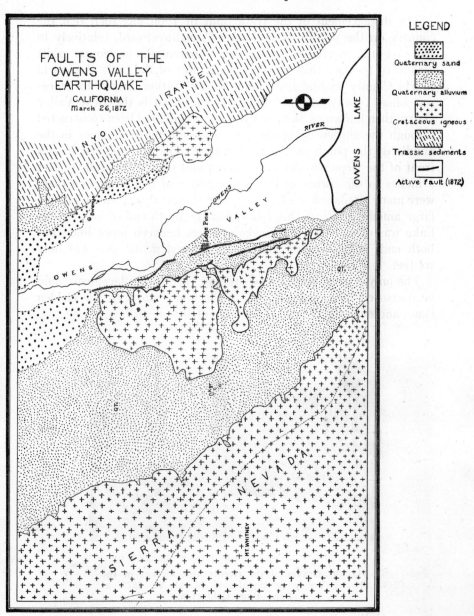

Fig. 38. Map of the Owens Valley Earthquake, March 26, 1872.

The displacement of the fresh fault of 1906 was such that the country on the southwest side moved northwestward, relatively to that on the northeast side. The differential, horizontal shift amounted to more than ten feet along most of the fault. A road in Marin County leading from Point Reyes Station toward Inverness was offset twenty-one feet. South of this road is the Bear Valley Dairy, then known as Skinner's Ranch. A walk had been constructed through the garden up to the steps opposite the front door in the middle of the porch on the ranch house. The fault passed just in front of the steps parallel to the porch and shifted the walk 15 feet 5 inches to the corner of the house. South of San Francisco there were many similar offsets but they were frequently accompanied by a large amount of drag. One fence near the north end of San Andrés Lake was offset more than seventeen feet between fence lines, but both ends were dragged so that the largest actual gap was only six feet.

The only part of the fault where any vertical displacement could be measured with certainty was in the region north of the Golden Gate, and even there, it nowhere amounted to a yard.

— Photo by Rev. James B. Macelwane, S.J.

Fig. 39. Graves of the twenty-nine victims of the Owens Valley earthquake of March 26, 1872, at Lone Pine, California.

Owens Valley Earthquake

Early on the morning of March 26, 1872, a very violent earthquake shook the southern part of the Owens Valley[2] in southern

— Photo by Rev. James B. Macelwane, S.J.

Fig. 40. Earthquake fault scarps in Owens Valley near Lone Pine, California. View looking north.

California. Every house in the village of Lone Pine was destroyed and twenty-nine out of possibly three hundred inhabitants were killed. Whitney,[3] who went over the ground two months after the earthquake, wrote in the *Overland Monthly:*

> All the way from Haiwee Meadows to Big Pine Creek we met frequent cracks in the earth, areas of sunken ground, depressions partly filled with water, and regions where motions of the surface soil had taken place, either in a vertical or horizontal direction. The direction of these fissures is almost always nearly parallel with that of the base of the mountains, although in a few instances they run diagonally across the valley. . . . There are several places in the Valley where fissures in the ground have crossed roads, ditches, and lines of fences and where evidence has been left of an actual moving of the ground horizontally, as well as vertically. One of these instances of horizontal motion is seen on the road from Bend City to Independence, about three miles east of the latter place. Here, according to a careful diagram of the locality, drawn by Captain Scoones, it appears that the road running east and west has been cut off by a fissure twelve feet wide, and the westerly portion of it carried eighteen feet to the south. The same thing was noticed by us at Lone Pine and Big Pine, with regard to fences and ditches, the horizontal distance through which the ground had been moved varying from three to twelve feet.

Gilbert,[4] who studied the effects eleven years later says:

> The principal scarp follows the alluvial foot slope of the Sierra Nevada, and has a maximum height of about twenty feet. Where this height is attained there is a companion fault scarp, ten feet high facing in the opposite direction, so that the net displacement is about ten feet.

The greatest displacements measured were twenty-three feet vertically and eighteen feet horizontally. The southern part of the Owens Valley, forty miles of which is traversed by this earthquake fault of

1872, is a long, narrow, V-shaped trench, partially filled with alluvial deposits, gravels and lake beds. The level of the present floor varies from 4002 feet at Big Pine on the north to 3569 feet at the surface of Owens Lake on the south. To the west rises the steep eastern fault scarp of the Sierra Nevada Mountains culminating, near Lone Pine, in Mount Whitney at 14,497 feet elevation. Thus, this abrupt, canyon-carved, glaciated, snow-crowned mass of Mesozoic igneous rock towers more than 10,800 feet above the floor of the Owens Valley. At the foot of the slope, forming an outlier of the Sierra Nevada, are the Alabama Hills of granite and Triassic sediments. It is along the eastern base of these hills that the fresh fault runs. The eastern wall of the valley is formed by the Inyo Range, which is composed of folded and faulted Paleozoic strata and Cretaceous quartz-monzonite and rises even more abruptly than the Sierras to a height above Owenyo of 11,125 feet. The crests of the two ranges are only about eighteen miles apart.

Hawaiian Earthquake

About a week before the Hawaiian earthquake[5] of April 2, 1868, a series of shocks began, some of which were strong enough to throw down stone walls and cause rock falls on the cliffs. The great earth-

— Photo by Rev. James B. Macelwane, S.J.

Fig. 41. Looking westward in the Owens Valley near Lone Pine, California. Fault scarp in the foreground, the Alabama Hills in the middle ground, and the Sierra Nevada with Mt. Whitney in the background.

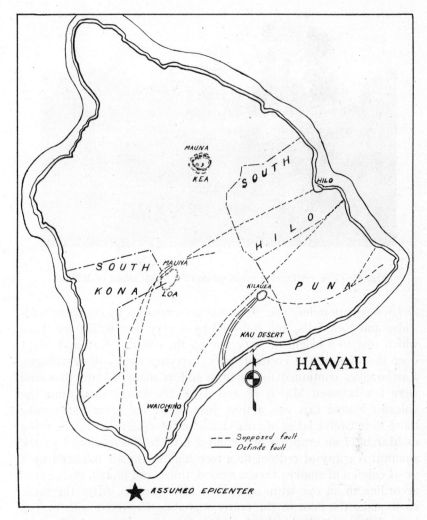

Fig. 42. Map of the Hawaiian Earthquake of April 2, 1868.

quake came about four o'clock in the afternoon. The ground swayed so violently that animals were overthrown and men had to brace themselves with hands and feet to prevent being rolled on the ground. In the district of Kau the earthquake was catastrophic and was little less violent in Kona, Puna, and Hilo. It was felt throughout the islands as far as Kauai more than 310 miles to the northwest of Kau. A circle of that radius would include an area of more than

— Photo by Harry O. Wood

Fig. 43. The earthquake crack of April 2, 1868, south of Kilauea.

289,500 square miles. The shock was accompanied by immense land-slides and rock falls, and followed by a very destructive sea wave which rose to a height of sixty feet on the coast of Kau and swept over the tops of the coconut trees, carrying away whole villages. Earthquakes continued for months and as many as two thousand were felt between March 27 and April 10. At the same time the volcano Mauna Loa was active. Just before the great earthquake there were twelve lakes of lava visible in the crater. On the morning of March 27 an eruption broke out a little to the southwest of the summit. A spray of red-hot lava rose high in the air followed by a great column of smoke; then a second, third, and fourth, giving rise, according to an eye witness, to four lava streams. After the great earthquake the floor of the crater was almost covered with molten lava. Kilauea had also been active for some months before the earthquake series began. The lava from Mauna Loa finally flowed out quietly on April 7 through a chasm which appears to have been opened during the great earthquake of April 2. This chasm is exactly in line with a sea cliff which, according to Wood, is a fault scarp and is associated with a great rift zone that extends entirely across the island from Waichinu to Hilo and passes through, or very close to, the caldera of Kilauea. Moreover there was indisputable evidence of relative horizontal displacement amounting to about twenty feet.

The whole series of events, seismic and volcanic, seems to be intimately related to and probably dependent upon regional stresses of a tectonic character.

Kwanto Earthquake

This is the name given to the Japanese earthquake[6] of September 1, 1923, which took such a huge toll of life and property and has been the subject of many scientific studies.[7] About one and one half minutes before noon the first slight shock started near the northern end of Sagami Bay and migrated southeastward. Then came the catastrophe. In a few seconds the towns about the bay were in

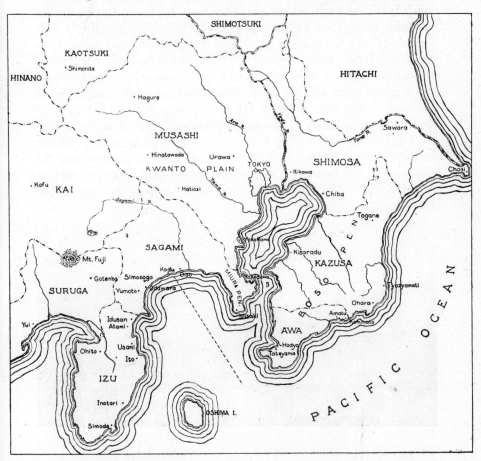

Fig. 44. Map of the Kwanto Japanese Earthquake, September 1, 1923.

ruins. To the north in the Kanagawa Prefecture, there were villages like Simosoga where ninety-eight per cent of the existing houses were totally destroyed. In the town of Yokosuka out of 16,245 buildings 8300 or 51.1 per cent totally collapsed, 2500 were partially destroyed, and 3500 were burned. In the city of Yokohama 11,615 buildings collapsed entirely, 7992, partially, and 58,981 were burned down. In the latter city 23,440 persons are known to have been killed and 42,053 injured. In the Tokyo Prefecture the city itself was the chief sufferer. Buildings to the number of 3886 were totally destroyed by the earthquake and 366,262 by the fire. The Tiba Prefecture on the Boso Peninsula east of Tokyo also suffered much from the earthquake. There were six towns on this peninsula in which more than eighty per cent of the buildings entirely collapsed. In the town of Hodyo near the southern end there were 1553 buildings, and of these 1502 collapsed completely. According to Imamura, in the whole devastated area, consisting principally of the Kwanto Plain and the Boso, Miura, and Izu Peninsulas, 576,262 buildings were destroyed, 99,331 people were killed, and 103,733 injured. The intensity of the earthquake was greatest at the northwest end of the Sagami Bay and on the alluvial plain at the southern end of the Boso Peninsula. The most marked effect on land was the elevation of the two eastern peninsulas and of the adjacent portion of the Kwanto Plain and the depression of the southern end of the Izu Peninsula.

— Photo by C. G. Dahm

Fig. 46. The white line at the base of this basin-range mountain is the Pleasant Valley Fault Scarp, Nevada.

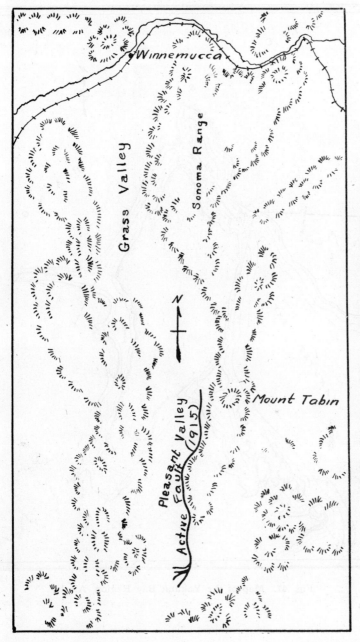

Fig. 45. Map of the Pleasant Valley Earthquake, October 2, 1915.

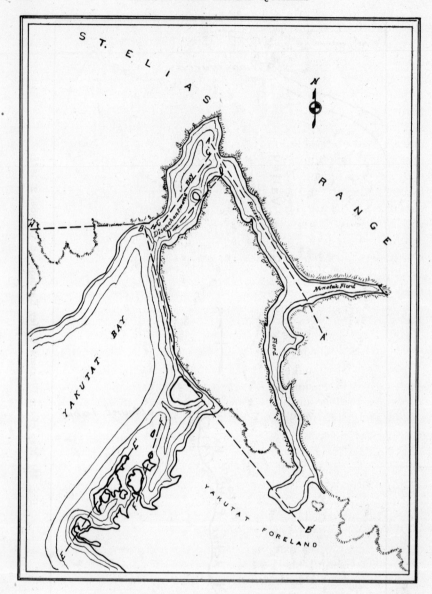

Fig. 47. Map of the Yakutat Bay Region, Alaska.

Pleasant Valley Earthquake

An earthquake[8] of great interest occurred shortly before eleven o'clock on Saturday night, October 2, 1915, in Pleasant Valley, Nevada. It was felt from Baker City, Oregon, to San Diego, California, and from the Pacific Coast to Salt Lake City, Utah. Slipping occurred on a fault at the base of the Sonoma Range on the east side of Pleasant Valley. From a point forty miles south of Winnemucca, Nevada, the fault scarp could be followed a distance of twenty-two miles in a southerly direction. It ranged from five to fifteen feet in height. There was almost no horizontal motion parallel to the strike of the fault. The striae on the fresh rock surface inclined less than five degrees to the north. The dip of the fault plane was fifty-four degrees due west, and the downthrow was on the west or valley side. The Sonoma Range is thought to be of the typical basin range type. Its west face is an eroded fault scarp. The fault of 1915 follows the old line very closely. Near the fault the range is composed almost exclusively of rhyolite and basalt.

Yakutat Bay Earthquake

In the late summer of the year 1899 there occurred in the Yakutat Bay[9] region of Alaska a number of severe shocks which culminated in a violent earthquake in the afternoon of September 10. Yakutat Bay, with its extensions, Disenchantment Bay and Russell Fiord, lies about forty miles southeast of Mount Saint Elias. Back of the bay to the northeast the Saint Elias Range, composed of metamorphic and crystalline rocks, rises within a very few miles to heights of 12,000 to 13,000 feet and within about fifty miles toward the north-northwest to 19,540 feet at the summit of Mount Logan. Abutting against these giants are lower mountains, 2000 to 6000 feet in elevation, which are composed mainly of shales, sandstones, and conglomerates of possible Mesozoic age. Stretching out into the ocean from the base of the latter group is a broad foreland of glacial detritus. Shallow sea extends fifty to sixty miles beyond to the edge of the continental shelf. Apparently at the time of the earthquakes, and probably by that of September 10, the intermediate mountain belt was raised up by varying amounts reaching a maximum of 47.3 feet on the west shore of Disenchantment Bay. At the same time a narrow belt of the foreland was depressed. The line between elevated and depressed areas follows the steep mountain front, which presents the appearance, with its truncated spurs,

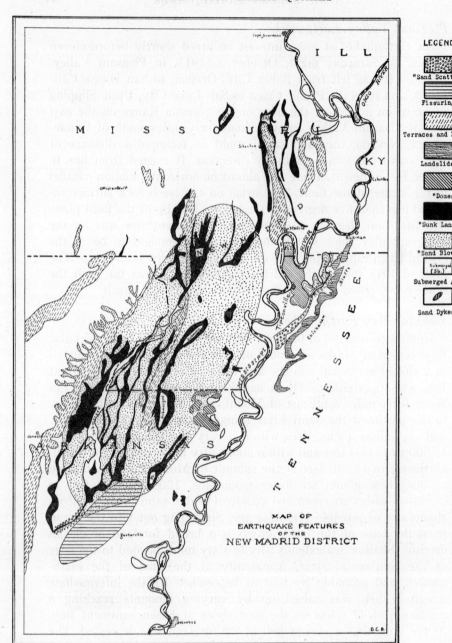

Fig. 48. Map of the New Madrid Earthquake of December 16, 1911.

of an older fault scarp. There appears, besides, to have been considerable movement on two nearly parallel faults in Disenchantment Bay, and also in Russell Fiord on the boundary fault between the conglomerates, shales, and sandstones of the Yakutat Group and the older rocks of the Saint Elias Range. A small nunatak at the head of Nunatak Fiord was traversed by a number of subsidiary parallel faults with vertical throws varying up to 7.9 feet. The earthquake of September 10 was very violent and was felt over an area extending from Sitka on the east to the mouth of Cook Inlet on the west and from the Pacific Coast on the south to the Yukon River on the north, more than 193,000 square miles. It was recorded by practically all seismographs then in operation over the world even in the neighborhood of the Alaskan antipodes.

New Madrid Earthquakes

The New Madrid, Missouri, earthquakes[10] occurred in the interval from December 16, 1811, to February 7, 1812. With no serious foreshocks, the people in that portion of the valley of the Mississippi River which surrounds New Madrid, Missouri, were roused from their sleep a little after two o'clock in the morning of December 16, 1811, by the roar of crashing furniture, cracking timbers, falling chimneys, landslides, and loud explosive sounds as the earth belched forth great volumes of sand and water. Groping in the darkness and crawling out of the debris of their fallen log cabins, the inhabi-

— Photo by M. L. Fuller. Courtesy U. S. Geol. Survey

Fig. 49. Stumps of timber killed by submergence in the New Madrid earthquake, December 16, 1811. Reelfoot Lake, Tennessee.

— Photo by M. L. Fuller. Courtesy U. S. Geol. Survey

Fig. 50. Cypress trees with double sets of roots at the
south end of Reelfoot Lake, Tennessee. Before the
New Madrid earthquake the water stood at the level of
the knees in the upper set.

tants were exposed to the winter cold. In the morning another severe
shock preceded by a low rumbling did further damage to the totter-
ing buildings, brought down more landslides, and opened new fissures. The earthquakes uplifted some areas and depressed others.
Waters were extruded from numberless cracks and craterlets. In the
Mississippi River, banks caved, islands sank, fissures opened in the
river bed, filled with water, then closed and spouted the water forth
thus forming dangerous waves. Boats on the river were sunk or
washed high upon the banks. Shocks of less severity occurred at frequent intervals. However, on the 23 of January and on the 7 of
February, 1812, the country was shaken by earthquakes of nearly
as great violence as those on December 16, 1811. A careful record
kept by Jared Brooks at Louisville, Kentucky, showed 1874 shocks
between December 16, 1811, and March 15, 1812, of which eight
were classed as violent and ten more as very severe. The aftershocks
continued for a long time.

The three principal earthquakes were felt over an area of more
than 1,000,000 square miles extending as far as the Atlantic seaboard and, it is said, even to Boston, stopping clocks, ringing bells

and cracking plaster in Virginia and the Carolinas. The area of greatest disturbance extended along the Mississippi River from Cairo, Illinois, to a point west of Memphis, Tennessee. The Paleozoic rocks which underlie the soft Tertiary and Quaternary deposits of the flood plains are known to be much faulted farther north where they approach the surface. The district is marked by minor faults, sunken lands, domes, sand blows, sand dikes, fissures, and lakes. Reelfoot Lake in Tennessee was produced by these earthquakes.

Charleston Earthquake

On Tuesday evening, August 31, 1886, shortly before ten p.m., local time, the city of Charleston, South Carolina, and the country surrounding it on the northwest were devastated by the worst earthquake[11] that has visited the Atlantic seaboard in historic times. It was felt from Canada to the Gulf of Mexico and from Bermuda westward into Iowa, Missouri, and Arkansas, and was reported to have broken windows in Milwaukee, Wisconsin. The disturbed area was about 2,800,000 square miles, one of the largest known in history; yet the damage was small in comparison. The city of Charleston suffered considerably. A little more than one hundred buildings were destroyed and ninety per cent of the brick structures were somewhat damaged. The region of greatest intensity seemed to lie along a NNE-SSW line about twelve miles west of the city of Charleston, between Woodstock and Rantowles. In that area even frame buildings were demolished. Cracks appeared in the soil. Large quantities of water and sand were ejected from fissures and craterlets. One of these craters at Ten Mile Hill on the South Carolina Railway was twenty-one feet broad. The railroad bed was flexed and alternately depressed and elevated; bolts were sheared off; ties were dragged or split; the rails were torn apart or kinked; and a train was derailed, overturned, and wrecked about one mile east of this same point. The greatest intensity along this railroad seemed to be near the station of Woodstock about sixteen miles northwest of Charleston. The greatest intensity on the Charleston and Savannah Railway was found to be in the vicinity of Rantowles Station, eighteen miles by railroad, or twelve miles as the crow flies, due west of Charleston. The Cretaceous and Tertiary deposits that overlie the Piedmont crystalline complex in the Coast Plain are, in general, poorly consolidated.

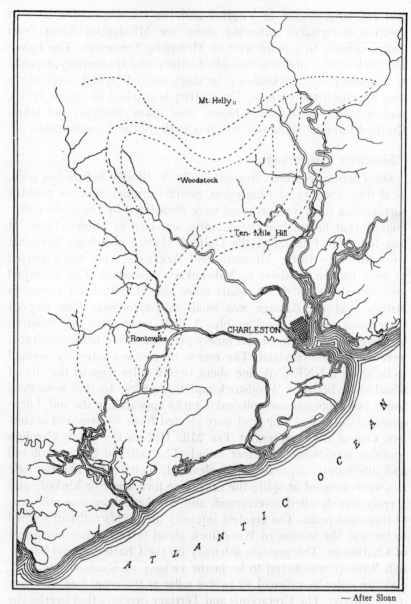

— After Sloan

Fig. 51. Lines of equal intensity. Dotted lines show area of highest
intensity.

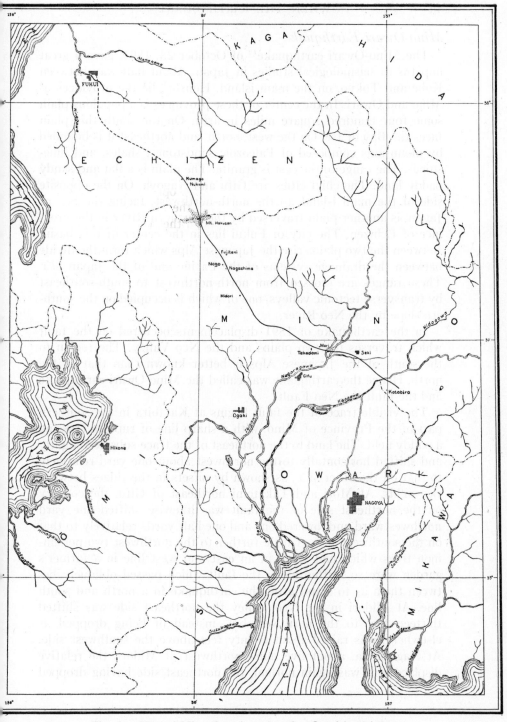

Fig. 52. Map of Mino-Owari earthquake, October 28, 1891.

Mino-Owari Earthquake

The Mino-Owari earthquake[12] of October 28, 1891, gave a great impetus to seismological studies in Japan. About half way between Kobe and Tokyo, on the main island, Honshu, lie the provinces of Mino and Owari. In the center of these provinces is a populous plain some four hundred square miles in area. On the south this plain faces the Bay of Ise. On the west, north, and northeast it is bounded by mountains composed of Paleozoic sandstones, shales, and limestones. The range to the east is granite. The plain is a flat and sandy paddy land. The chief cities are Gifu and Nagoya. On the opposite side of the main island, to the north-northwest, facing the Sea of Japan, is another plain traversed by the Kuzuryu River in the province of Echizen. The city of Fukui lies in the center of this basin. Between the two plains rise the Japanese Alps which form the divide between the drainage systems of the Pacific and of the Japan Sea. These ranges are crossed from north-northwest to south-southeast by transverse tectonic valleys, one of which is occupied on the southern slope by the Neo River.

In the earthquake of 1891 displacements occurred on the fault which traverses the two plains and the Neo Valley. The region to the south of the Japanese Alps is better known than that to the north. Hence the earthquake was called the Mino-Owari earthquake and the fault the Neo Fault.

The visible trace of the fault begins at Katabira in the southern part of the Province of Mino, with a sharp line of rupture crossing a paddy field. The land to the northeast of the trace subsided slightly and shifted horizontally to the northwest about one yard relatively to that on the other side, as shown by offsets in the ridges between rice fields. At Mori and Takatomi northeast of Gifu, the country on the northeast side of the fault was likewise shifted one yard northwestward and lowered one and one half yards relatively to that on the southwest side. A little further to the northwest two persimmon trees which had stood in an east and west line in a farmer's garden were so shifted along the fault which passed obliquely between them as to stand after the earthquake in a north and south line. At Midori in the Neo Valley the northeast side was shifted thirteen feet to the northwest but, instead of being dropped as elsewhere, was raised about twenty feet above the southwest side. At Nagashima, about five miles northwest of Midori, the relative displacement was again normal, the northeast side having dropped three feet and shifted six feet northwestward. It is thought that the reversal of vertical shift at Midori represents an arch due to local compression. The fissure left the Neo Valley at Nogo and passed through Fujitani with the northeast side depressed and shifted northwestward. Six miles farther it crossed Shijugara Ridge into a branch of the Tokunoyama Valley parallel to the Neo Valley on the west; then it cut through the eastern shoulder of Mount Hakusan on the boundary between the provinces of Mino and Echizen, passed through Nukumi and Eumago where the horizontal shift amounted to ten feet, crossed over the Minomata Pass, and continued down the bed of the Asuwagawa.

The total land area shaken in this earthquake was greater than 94,000 square miles, and the damage done was very considerable.

Tango Earthquake

Honshu, the main island of the Japanese archipelago, is markedly convex toward the Pacific Ocean and concave toward the Sea of Japan. Where the shore of the latter swings sharply westward, it is indented by Wakasa Bay. The Tango peninsula heading in a northeasterly direction incloses this bay on its northwestern side. Here, March 7, 1927, occurred an earthquake[13] that rivaled in severity and destruction the Kwanto earthquake of 1923. It began in early evening precisely at twenty-seven minutes and forty-six seconds after nine o'clock Greenwich mean time according to Hodgson.[14] In Mineyama and neighboring towns more than 14,000 buildings were destroyed and 2908 persons were killed, according to the official report of the Japanese government. At the same time there appeared *en echelon* across the neck of the Tango peninsula a series of fresh scarps on the Gomura fault, and almost immediately another series formed on the Yamada fault at right angles to the first and parallel with the southeastern shore of the peninsula. The land on the southwest of the Gomura fault was raised up and shifted southeastward relatively to that on the northeast side of the fault, the maximum horizontal shift being two hundred and eighty-one centimeters (9.2 feet) in the village of Gomura and the maximum vertical displacement being seventy-nine centimeters (2.6 feet). The fault was found to dip about seventy degrees toward the southwest and is therefore a reverse fault. The land to the northwest of the Yamada fault was raised seventy centimeters (2.3 feet) and shifted toward the northeast eighty centimeters (2.6 feet), relatively to that on the southeast

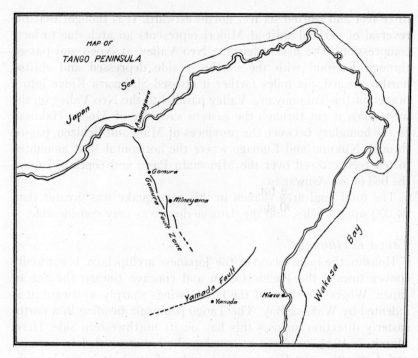

Fig. 53. Map of the Tango Earthquake, March 7, 1927.

side of the fault. Precise leveling and triangulation, according to
Tsuboi,[15] proved the production of a flexure or disguised fault zone
roughly parallel to the Gomura fault and farther toward the southwest. On the block between this zone and the Gomura fault, the
shore of the Sea of Japan was uplifted about eighty centimeters (2.6
feet) while the elevation of the shore to the northeast of the Gomura
fault was not altered. A masterly stereometric study of the positions
of the foci or origins of the more than four hundred aftershocks
observed with portable seismographs suitably placed led Imamura
and Nasu[16] to the conclusion that the three above-mentioned fault
zones, together with a fourth hypothetical one whose trace would
lie under the Sea of Japan, bound a prismatic block which was
squeezed or pinched up in the earthquake somewhat like the shoot-
ing of an apple seed by squeezing between the fingers. The aftershocks occurred mostly in the rocks immediately surrounding the
block, whereas, according to Hodgson, the main rupture began on

the Gomura fault near the base of the block. Igneous rocks cover
the greater part of the surface of the block and its surroundings,
according to Tsuya,[17] much of it being granite.

Wellington Earthquake

New Zealand consists principally of two large islands, known as
North Island and South Island. They are traversed from northeast
to southwest by mountain chains. These mountains are composed

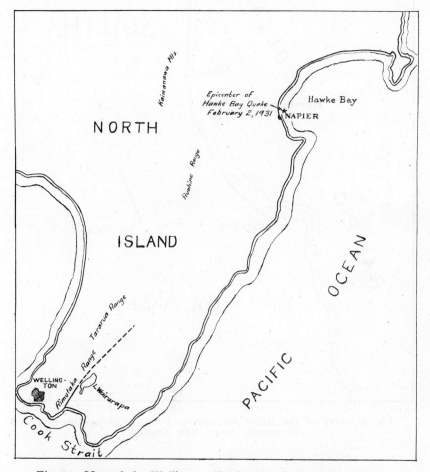

Fig. 54. Map of the Wellington Earthquake, January 23, 1855, and
of the Hawke Bay earthquake, February 2, 1931.

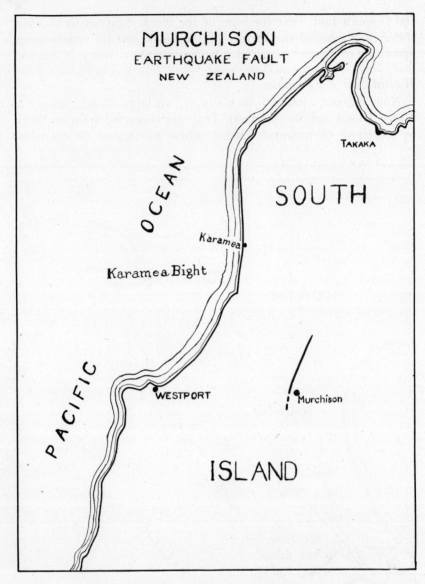

Fig. 55.　Map of the Buller earthquake, June 17, 1929, Murchison
Earthquake Fault, New Zealand.

of Permo-Jurassic fluvio-marine argillites, sandstones, and conglomerates of the Hokonui system. At the foot of the Rimutaka Mountains on the southeast, and separated from the Hokonui rocks of that range by the great Wairarapa or Clarence Fault, lie the unconsolidated postglacial deposits of the Wairarapa Plain. This plain and the mountains are both cut off abruptly by Cook Strait.

On January 23, 1855, a violent earthquake[18] elevated the Rimutaka Mountains leaving a fresh scarp along the Wairarapa Fault for a distance of ninety miles. The elevation above high tide of a white band of coral-like millepores along the cliffs on Cook Strait showed that the Rimutaka Mountains had been uplifted about ten feet while the level of the Wairarapa Plain remained unchanged. Proceeding westward along the coast from the end of the scarp, the uplift of the Rimutaka block was found to decrease gradually, becoming imperceptible at sixteen miles beyond Wellington. Thus, during the earthquake, there was uplifted and tilted westward a tract ninety miles long and twenty-three miles wide.

More recent destructive earthquakes in New Zealand were the Buller earthquake[19] of June 17, 1929, in the South Island and the Hawke Bay earthquake[20] of February 2, 1931, on the east coast of North Island. In the former there occurred a displacement on a fault about seven miles west of Murchison in which the ground on the east side of the fault was raised fifteen feet and shifted northwestward nine feet relatively to that on the west side. The Hawke Bay earthquake caused great damage at Napier, Hastings, and other neighboring towns. It originated under the western part of Hawke Bay and quite close to the city of Napier.

Cutch Earthquake

At the western end of India is the Province of Sindh, through which flows the River Indus with its many mouths spreading over a wide delta. To the southeast of this delta one of the channels, the Kori, separates the Island of Cutch from Sindh. East of the delta of the Indus is the desert of Parkar; and between it and Cutch stretches the curious Rann of Cutch, a wide area but little above sea level which is marsh and salt desert by turns. The upper part of the Kori channel is known as the Puran and formerly traversed the northwest corner of the Rann. On the 16 of June, 1819, there occurred a violent earthquake[21] which was felt all across India as far as Calcutta and Pondicherry. A very considerable area northeast of Lakhpat was depressed and immediately flooded by the sea water which rushed in through the Kori. At the same time the people who happened to be in the fortress of Sindri on the margin of the Rann saw, about four miles to the north, a long barrier stretch itself across what was formerly a plain. They called it the Allah Bund or Dam of Allah. It was in reality a fault whose surface expression was a flexure in the surface alluvium. The portion of the plain to the

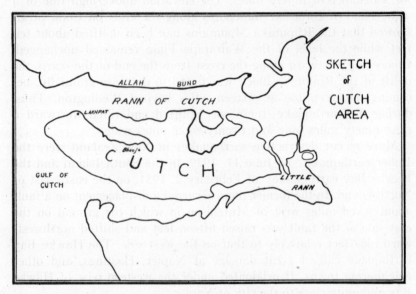

Fig. 56. Map of the Cutch earthquake in the Province of Sindh, India, June 18, 1819.

north had been elevated and that to the south had been depressed relatively to one another through a height of twenty feet. The Bund is said to be at least fifty miles in length. In 1844 Captain Baker of the Bengal Engineers made a profile across the Bund and found that the land to the north was actually elevated by the earthquake and that it slopes downward away from the Bund, while that to the south of the Bund was depressed to form the bottom of the basin of Sindri and that it slopes upward toward the south away from that barrier.

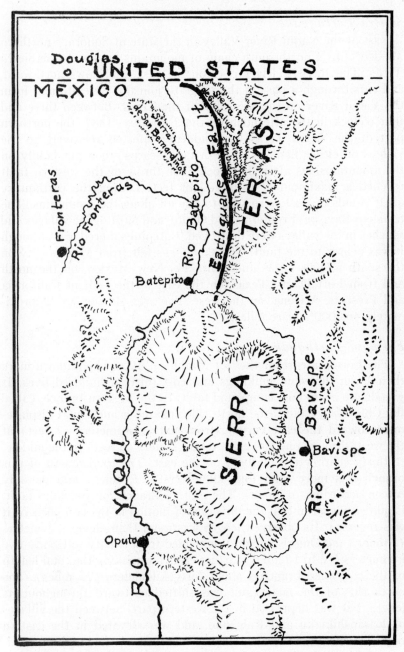

Fig. 57. Map of the Sonora, Mexico, earthquake, May 3, 1887.

Sonora Earthquake

East of the Yaqui River Valley in the state of Sonora,[22] northern Mexico, runs a north-south chain of mountains known as the Sierra Teras. The Bavispe River rises on the east side, flows northward, and cuts through a pass in the range to join the Batepito and form the Yaqui River on the west side of the Teras. Between three and four o'clock in the afternoon on the 3 of May, 1887, the northern part of the Sierra Teras was suddenly uplifted relatively to the valleys on either flank. The fresh fault scarps stood out boldly on the mountainsides after the shock. The throw of the western fault reached a maximum of twenty-eight feet. During the earthquake great clouds of dust were seen to rise all along the mountains. The towns of Bavispe, Fronteras, and Oputo, and most of the villages and ranches in the valleys were destroyed. Batepito suffered less although it was nearer to the fault. The shock was felt from Mexico City on the south to Las Vegas and Santa Fe, New Mexico, on the north and from Fort Davis, Texas, on the east to the Gulf of California and Prescott, Arizona, on the west. The area shaken was approximately 464,000 square miles.

Formosa Earthquake

The Formosa earthquake[23] of March 17, 1906, shook down more than seven thousand buildings and cost thirteen hundred lives. It was due to a slip on a compound fault. In the western branch, called the Chinsekiryo fault, the north side suffered a horizontal displacement toward the east varying from sixty centimeters (2 feet) at the west, through one and eight-tenths meters (6 feet) in the middle, to thirty centimeters (1 foot) on the east. The total length of this branch was more than four kilometers (2.5 miles) and possibly fifteen according to Omori. The eastern branch, or Baishiko fault, is quite unusual in that the direction of motion in the two parts of it was reversed. Its observed length was more than eleven kilometers (7 miles) and Omori thought it extended from twenty to twenty-five kilometers (12 to 16 miles) farther east thus making the total length of the combined branches about forty kilometers (25 miles). The north side of the main fault was shifted eastward throughout its length, but was depressed in the western part, between the villages of Kasanshikiaku and Kaigenko, and was elevated in the eastern part. The maximum vertical displacement was six feet and the maximum horizontal shift was eight feet.

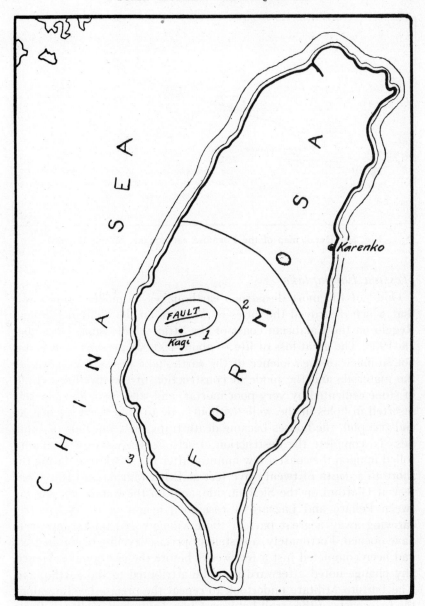

Fig. 58. Map of the Formosa earthquake, March 17, 1906.

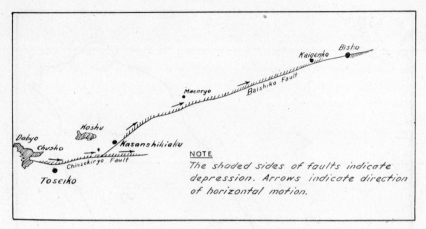

Fig. 59. Detail map of the Formosa earthquake, March 17, 1906.

Messina Earthquake

One[24] of the most disastrous earthquakes of modern times was
that which destroyed the cities of Messina on the Sicilian side and
Reggio on the Calabrian coast of the Strait of Messina, December
28, 1908. The great loss of life — about 100,000 persons — was due
not so much to the violence of the earthquake in itself as it was to
the materials and the mode of construction of the dwellings. Built
of stone cemented by very poor mortar, and with floor joists merely
inserted in holes in the walls without a tie to hold them against an
endwise pull, the houses became death traps for thousands of families. To complete the destruction, a seismic sea wave or tsunami[25]
rolled in upon the coast a few minutes after the shock inundating the
shore to a depth of twenty-five feet at Priga Marina and thirty-one
feet at Giardini on the Sicilian side; and on the Calabrian side between Pellaro and Lazzaro it rose to a height of thirty-five feet
carrying away a great part of those villages. No faults appear to
have opened. Fortunately, a system of precise leveling begun in 1898
had been completed just a few weeks before the earthquake. Hence,
any change noted afterward must be attributed to the earthquake.
The Istituto Militare undertook to repeat the precise leveling along
the two coasts of the strait between Gioia Tauro and Melito di Porto
Salvo, a distance of fifty-four miles on the Calabrian side. They did
the same on the Sicilian side for a distance of eight miles along the
sea between Messina and Faro Peloro, and back twelve miles to

Gessa and nearly fourteen miles to Castanea. It was found that strong downwarping had occurred in the strait. The Calabrian shore had subsided by varying amounts between Scylla and Lazzaro. At San Giovanni the subsidence was thirty centimeters (12 inches), at Reggio forty-three centimeters (17 inches). On the Sicilian side, the subsidence of the coast at Messina was calculated to be sixty-

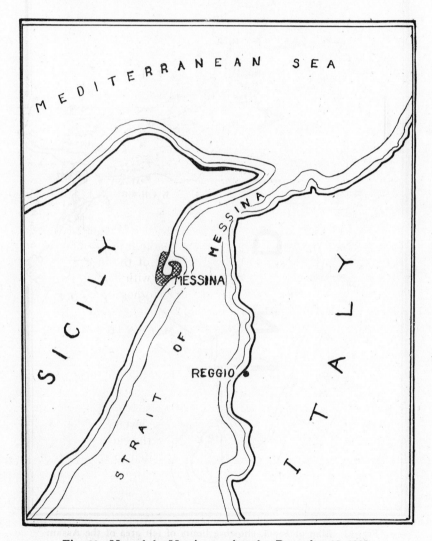

Fig. 60. Map of the Messina earthquake, December 28, 1908.

seven centimeters (26 inches) but dropped to eight centimeters (3 inches) on the Tertiary rocks six and five-tenths kilometers (4 miles) inland. Novarese[26] argued from this fact and from the lack of tie to the crystalline rocks in the leveling on the Calabrian side

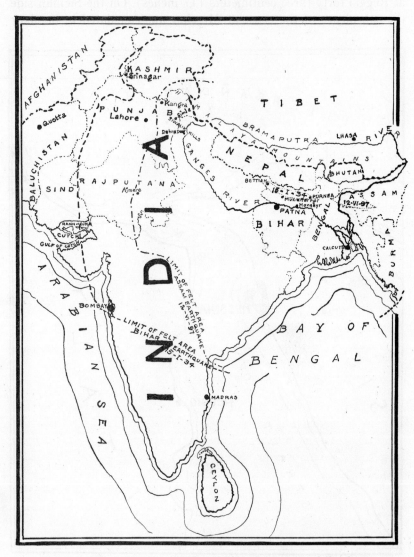

Fig. 61. Map of India, showing limits of felt area of the Assam and Bihar earthquakes.

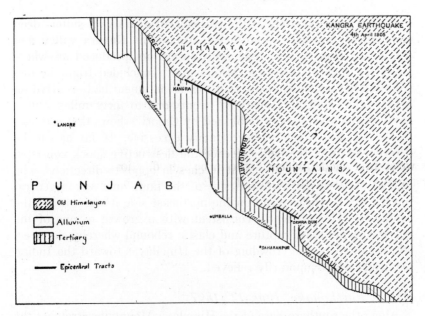

Fig. 62. Map of the Kangra earthquake, April 4, 1905.

that the movement was entirely confined to the unconsolidated Quaternary deposits along the coast without disturbing the crystalline basement and was of the nature of a landslide toward deep water. But this seems very improbable.

Kangra Earthquake

About ten minutes after six o'clock, Madras time, on the morning of April 4, 1905, or ten minutes before one, Greenwich time, there occurred a destructive earthquake in the foothills of the Himalaya mountains[27] in the northeastern Punjab which took about 20,000 lives and was felt over an area of approximately 1,625,000 square miles from Afghanistan to Bengal.

The main epicentral tract extended toward the southeast from Kangra, while a secondary tract, within which the damage was only slightly less severe, lay about one hundred and fifty miles farther toward the southeast in the neighborhood of Dehra Dun. Both tracts lie in the zone of overthrust faulting along the Himalayan mountain front. In general the Great Boundary Fault is convex toward the

58   WHEN THE EARTH QUAKES

southwest; but precisely at the two epicentral tracts it suffers deep
embayments toward the northeast around the Kangra valley and
the Dehra Dun. Visible fault scarps were not produced anywhere
along the zone of thrusting. Middlemiss[28] concluded from the distribution of surface intensity that the displacement had occurred on
a low angle fault at a depth of twenty-one to forty miles. But a
study of the seismograms published by Omori[29] shows that estimate
of the depth of focus to be certainly excessive. As far as can be
determined from the field evidence the destructive shock consisted
of two or three sudden, violent lurches in opposite directions. The
first of these on the southwest side of the fault zone was in general
toward the northeast; and on the northeast side it was toward the
southwest. This is clearly consistent with a growth of one of the
overthrust faults by rupture and elastic rebound whereby the overstrain caused by the crowding of the Himalayas toward the Indian
peninsula was temporarily relieved.

Assam Earthquake, June 12, 1897

Along the southern base of the Himalaya Mountains stretches the
broad, alluvial plain of the Ganges River. The Brahmaputra River

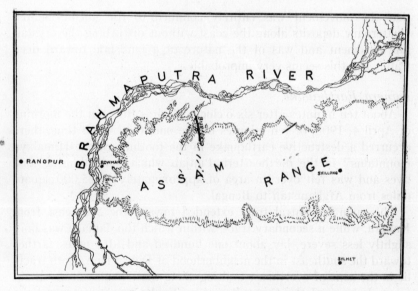

Fig. 63. Map of the Assam earthquake (detail), June 12, 1897.

rises on the northern flanks of the Himalayas, flows far to the east through the highlands of Tibet, turns southward into eastern Assam, then flows in a westerly direction through that country and finally turns southward once more and joins the Ganges in eastern Bengal. South of the alluvial valley of the Brahmaputra, and between it and the plain of Sylhet, the hills of the Assam Range rise to a height of about four thousand feet. They are a series of recently uplifted and tilted fault blocks whose scarps run in a more or less east and west direction. Their summits are formed by extensive remnants of an older peneplain separated by the steep-walled canyons of the marginal drainage systems, cut subsequent to the uplift. The hills are composed of crystalline and metamorphic rocks with the folded edges of Cretaceous and Tertiary sedimentary formations on their southern border.

It was in this tilted block region that the Great Indian earthquake[30] of June 12, 1897, occurred. Between five and six o'clock in the afternoon the whole hill region was apparently moved to the north and was relatively elevated by amounts ranging from two to seven meters, according to the results of a partial re-triangulation carried out the following winter. On the northern margin of the hills there occurred a transverse fault striking NNW and SSE and partially following the canyon of the Chedrang River, a tributary of the Krishnai. This fault could be followed a distance of twelve miles. Its plane was nearly vertical. The downthrow, which was invariably on the east side of the fault, varied from zero to more than thirty-five feet. The destruction wrought by the earthquake was terrible. Practically all masonry in Shillong and the other hill towns was leveled to the ground. Fissures opened; forests were destroyed; hillsides and canyon walls were scarred by landslides; drainage was blocked and impounded, forming lakes of considerable size. The lowlands of the Brahmaputra Valley and the Sylhet plain were dotted with blow holes and sand craters. Whole districts of jungle and farm land were flooded, drowning the trees and crops; while other areas of swampy ground were drained. Extensive damage was done to buildings from Calcutta and the Bay of Bengal to Tibet and from Nepal and Bihar to the confines of Burma, an area of about 148,000 square miles. The shock was felt from Rangoon to Ajmere and the Punjab. The total area over which it was sensible is estimated at 1,750,000 square miles.

Baluchistan Earthquake

In the early morning of December 20, 1892, the greater portion of Baluchistan was shaken by an earthquake[31] which did great damage to buildings, bridges, railroads, and other structures. It was caused, according to Griesbach, by movement on a fault on the west flank of the Kojak range of mountains, passing along the Northwestern Railway at Shalabagh and Sanzal. The new break followed an old line of dislocation marked by rift features, springs, and fault breccia. The west or valley side subsided about eight to ten inches and shifted southward relatively to the east side a distance of two to two and one-half feet as shown by the buckling and shortening of rails and pipes which crossed diagonally and by offsets of roads and irrigation ditches.

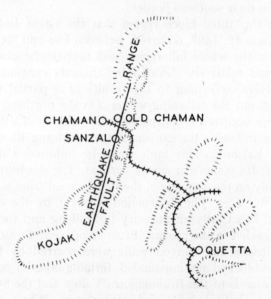

Fig. 64. Sketch map of the Baluchistan earthquake of December 20, 1892.

Bihar-Nepal Earthquake

In the afternoon of January 15, 1934, at thirteen minutes after two, India Standard Time, or forty-three minutes after eight, Greenwich, the province of Bihar in northern India and the kingdom of Nepal were visited by an earthquake of catastrophic intensity.[32]

There were three zones within which the loss of life and destruction of property reached a maximum. The largest of these tracts lay to the north of Muzaffarpur and Darbanga. The second was at Monghyr south of the Ganges River and the third was in the valley of Nepal southeast of Katmandu and included the town of Bhatgaon. Both Monghyr and Bhatgaon were almost totally destroyed. Around and including the main zone or epicentral tract a *slump belt* extended from near Bettiah on the northwest to Purnea on the southeast, a distance of nearly two hundred miles. Within this area

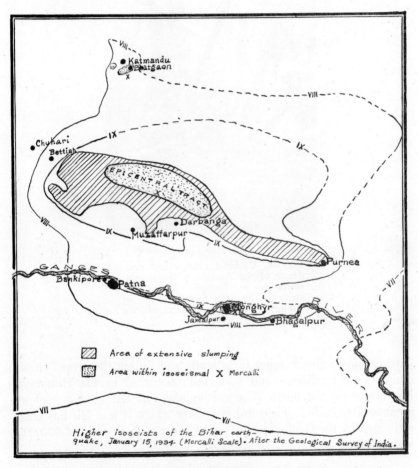

Fig. 65. Map of the epicentral region of the Bihar-Nepal earthquake of January 15, 1934.

scarcely a house of any weight escaped tilting and sinking. Roads and embankments subsided; depressions were filled and the whole countryside was covered by sand and water vents, craters, and gaping fissures. Immense quantities of water were extruded, carrying along with it sand and mud which covered the soil to a depth of a

— Courtesy Jesuit Mission Press

Fig. 66. Catholic church and residence of the American Jesuit missionaries in Bettiah, India, destroyed by the earthquake of January 15, 1934. Ruins of the church.

yard or more, thus ruining farm lands and killing the crops. Great numbers of landslides and rock falls occurred in the Himalaya Mountains on the north. The earthquake was felt at distances as great as 1000 miles. The total area over which it was felt has been estimated by the Geological Survey of India at upwards of 1,900,000 square miles.

— Courtesy Jesuit Mission Press

Fig. 66a. Catholic church and residence of the American Jesuit missionaries in Bettiah, India, destroyed by the earthquake of January 15, 1934. Ruined residence with damaged knitting school in the background.

— Courtesy Jesuit Mission Press

Fig. 66b. Catholic church and residence of the American Jesuit missionaries in Bettiah, India, destroyed by the earthquake of January 15, 1934. Ruins of the church.

— Courtesy Jesuit Mission Press

— Courtesy Jesuit Mission Press

Fig. 67. Catholics of Chudhari, India, on the ruins of their church after the earthquake of January 15, 1934.

Fig. 67a. Father F. Brown, S.J., in the ruins of his mission in Chuhari, India, after the earthquake of January 15, 1934.

— Courtesy Jesuit Mission Press

Fig. 68. In the slump belt of the earthquake of January 15, 1934, at Motihari, India.

— Photos by Rev. John Morrison, S.J. Courtesy Jesuit Mission Press

Fig. 69. The ruined city of Monghyr, India, after the earthquake of January 15, 1934.

— Photo by Rev. John Morrison, S.J. Courtesy Jesuit Mission Press

Fig. 69a. The ruined city of Monghyr, India, after earthquake
of January 15, 1934.

— Courtesy Jesuit Mission Press

Fig. 70. Severe damage to St. Joseph's Convent and Orphan Asylum in
Banipore, a suburb of Patna, India, by the earthquake of January 15, 1934.

— Courtesy Jesuit Mission Press

Fig. 71. Jamalpur, India, after the earthquake of January 15, 1934. Ruined dwellings.

— Courtesy Jesuit Mission Press

Fig. 71a. Jamalpur, India, after the earthquake of January 15, 1934. St. Joseph's Catholic Church.

Chapter III

KINDS OF EARTHQUAKES

The earthquakes described in the foregoing chapter do not in any sense exhaust the list of the destructive shocks of modern times. These word pictures are given the reader to furnish him with an album of illustrations, as it were, so that he will have an empirical foundation for the classification and further study of earthquakes in general.

What is an earthquake? An earthquake may be defined technically as a shaking of the earth's surface caused by a sudden disturbance of the elastic equilibrium of the rock masses in or beneath the crust of the earth.

Earthquakes according to this general definition may be classified in various ways. An earthquake is said to be *natural* if the disturbance and the consequent mass movements which give rise to the elastic vibrations or waves are caused by natural processes in the earth. It is said to be *artificial* if the disturbance was caused by man, as through a blast of explosives. Natural earthquakes are *perceptible* or *imperceptible* accordingly as the vibrations are felt by human beings, or can be detected only by suitable instruments. They are *local, near,* or *distant* according to the geographical location of their source relative to the observer. Perceptible earthquakes are *slight, strong, violent,* or *catastrophic* according to the intensity of the vibrations and the extent of the damage caused by them. These classifications have been introduced merely for purposes of description and convenience. They are obviously not meant to be exclusive. Thus the same earthquake will be near to one observer and distant from another. A catastrophic earthquake will grade off to imperceptibility with distance from the source.

Natural earthquakes are also classified as *shallow, normal,* or *deep* according to the vertical position of their source in relation to the surface of the earth. Shallow and deep are obviously relative terms; but because of the great preponderance of strong earthquakes which seem to originate at depths between five and twenty miles, this range is usually taken as the normal depth and an earthquake will be said to be shallow if it has its source much nearer to the surface of the earth than five miles, and it will be said to be deep if its source lies much farther down than twenty miles. The latter class is often subdivided into *intermediate* and *very deep* shocks.

Natural earthquakes are also classified as *tectonic, volcanic,* or *plutonic* according as the stresses which cause the movement are structural in origin, proceed from volcanic activity, or as they are deep-seated. Volcanic earthquakes are mostly very shallow, tectonic earthquakes are predominantly normal, and plutonic earthquakes always originate beneath the discontinuity at the base of the earth's crust.

The last of these classifications is most important for an understanding of earthquake phenomena. Hence we shall discuss each of those three classes in greater detail.

TECTONIC EARTHQUAKES

General Characteristics

Looking back over the preceding chapter, we see that the San Francisco, Pleasant Valley, Owens Valley, Mino-Owari, Baluchistan, Cutch, Sonora, Formosa, Tango, Wellington, and Murchison earthquakes have one thing in common. They all evidently involved a relative movement of the rocks on the two sides of a fracture or fault plane in the earth's crust. This fracture or fault plane was visible at the surface of the ground, the relative displacement could be and was actually measured and the intensity of the felt vibrations decreased rapidly with distance from the fault. Furthermore, the Wellington, Yakutat Bay, Messina, Kwanto, Tango, and Hawke Bay earthquakes involved striking changes of level measurable with reference to the sea. On the other hand, the Assam earthquake was accompanied by visible warping, and some parts of the New Madrid area were raised and others lowered without the production of a clear-cut fault scarp; but in these cases the surface was composed of soft, unconsolidated materials, and the warping was very probably the surface expression of a fault or faults in the harder rocks below.

Earthquakes that involve a sudden deformation of the earth's crust by faulting or warping are called *tectonic* (from the Greek τέκτων, a builder) because they are structural in character. This class probably also includes most of the shocks of less intensity, for in the majority of slight shocks we find that: (1) The area of greatest intensity often lies along a known fault zone; (2) they occur far from any volcano; (3) even in the neighborhood of an active volcano, they are often not correlated with any particular sign of volcanic activity; (4) they often associate themselves in groups in which the center of intensity of successive earthquakes migrates parallel to a fault zone. Furthermore, since rocks are known to be elastic, any sudden slip on a fault plane must generate earthquake waves. Difference in speed and in amplitude or range of mass movement and in the quantity of rock moved by the faulting will account

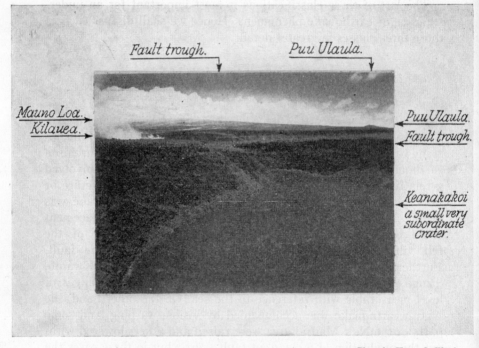

— Photo by Harry O. Wood

Fig. 72. The Hawaiian volcano Kilauea in the left middle ground, Mauna Loa in the left background; in the right foreground is Keanakakoi, a small subordinate crater. Running across the picture in the middle ground will be seen two conspicuous *fault troughs*.

Fig. 73. Explosions in the crater of Vesuvius. The slight tremors which accompanied these explosions were recorded by seismographs at the observatory high on the slope of the mountain; but they were not perceptible to the senses even on the crater rim.

for any observed variation in the over-all intensity of earthquake shocks, from the slightest tremor to the greatest catastrophe.

The character of the earthquake is not so obvious if there is no fault displacement or differential warping visible at the surface. Movements occurring in a horizontal thrust plane or on a low angle fault would be distinctly of the tectonic type and yet they might not cause relative surface displacements that would be measurable.

VOLCANIC EARTHQUAKES

Definition

Earthquakes may be associated with volcanoes in three ways: (1) An earthquake may originate in the neighborhood of an active or dormant volcano; (2) it may occur simultaneously with an eruption; (3) it may be caused by volcanism; — that is to say, the connection may be geographical, chronological, or genetic. Now the theory of Humboldt[33] that all seismic and volcanic phenomena are genetically interrelated and that both earthquakes and volcanoes are due to pressures operating in great reservoirs of molten rock at considerable depths has long since been abandoned by seismologists and geologists. Also the possibility cannot be excluded that a regional strain in the solid rock may culminate in fracture and elastic rebound and hence result in a tectonic earthquake along a zone of weakness in the vicinity of a volcano. Therefore it seems reasonable to restrict the term *volcanic earthquake* to such shocks as are causally dependent on volcanism. A volcanic earthquake, then, may be defined as a transient elastic vibration caused by forces originating in the magma chamber and conduits of a volcano. It may be due to an explosion, tension fracture, or fault within the structure of the volcano, and may be produced by the pressure of confined gases or by forces brought into play through the tumescence or withdrawal of lava.

— Photo courtesy Harry O. Wood

Fig. 74. Mauna Loa at sunset from the northeast rim of Kilauea.

Characteristics

Volcanic earthquakes are usually of considerable local intensity but of slight total energy. They may do extreme damage on the flank of the volcano or near its crater and yet be nearly or quite imperceptible a few miles away from its base. A tectonic earthquake of the same epicentral intensity would be recorded by seismographs at great distances. Volcanic earthquakes are frequently not recorded by sensitive seismographs in the vicinity. Earthquakes often occur in large numbers before, during, or after an eruption.

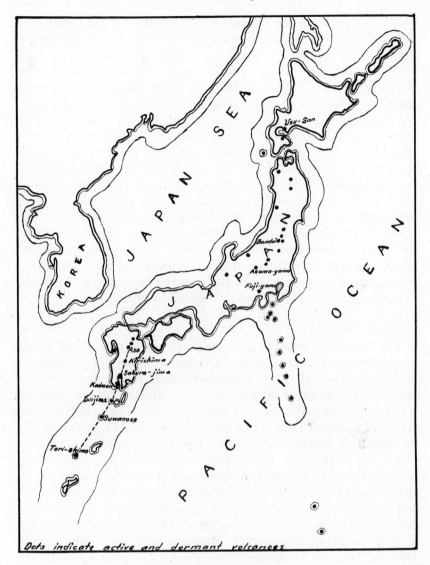

Fig. 75. Volcanoes of Japan.

Mauna Loa

The 1914 eruption[34] of the volcano Mauna Loa in the southern part of the island of Hawaii (Fig. 42) followed a quiet interval of almost eight years. The outbreak was first observed about 4 p.m.,

November 25, 1914. Almost two months earlier, on the morning of September 27, the automatic starting device on one of the seismographs at the Hawaiian Volcano Observatory began to make contact so frequently that it was impossible for some time to stop and reset the power clock. The pen on the only seismograph then in adjustment was observed to be swaying to and fro through wide arcs. These earthquake shocks were not felt at the observatory which is twenty-two miles from the summit crater of Mauna Loa in a direction slightly south of east but 9690 feet lower in elevation. Neither were any of the eleven shocks felt which were recorded during the next forty-eight hours. But at Kapapala, about fifteen miles southwest of the observatory, twenty-nine shocks were felt during a similar period, some of them being sharp. Altogether more than one hundred earthquakes were recorded up to the morning of November 25. Then, in less than two hours, twelve or more shocks were registered. The first three or four of this group came in quick succession and occurred approximately at the time the herdsmen at Kapapala first saw the fumes rising from the summit of Mauna Loa.

Usu-san Volcano

The Usu-san is situated near the southwest corner of the island of Hokkaido (or Yezzo), Japan. A violent eruption[35] of this volcano began July 25, 1910. Local earthquakes were felt in the vicinty on July 21. The town of Nishi-Monbets is situated on the shore of Volcano Bay at a distance of a little more than five miles from the center of Usu-san. Twenty-five shocks were felt in that town on the 22 and 110 shocks on the 23. The police thereupon ordered evacuation of the town. On the following day the number of shocks increased to 351. But after the beginning of the eruption on the 25 the earthquake frequency began to decrease so that the total number felt on the 25 was only 162. Of all these earthquakes felt at Nishi-Monbets only one on the 21 was strong enough to be recorded by a fairly sensitive seismograph at Sapporo, fourty-four miles distant from the volcano. There were three shocks strong enough to be recorded on the 22, twenty-three on the 23, seventy-six on the 24; while on the 25, the first day of the eruption, eighty-four were recorded. The two strongest shocks occurred on the 24 and 25, thirty hours and five and one-half hours respectively before the first volcanic eruption.

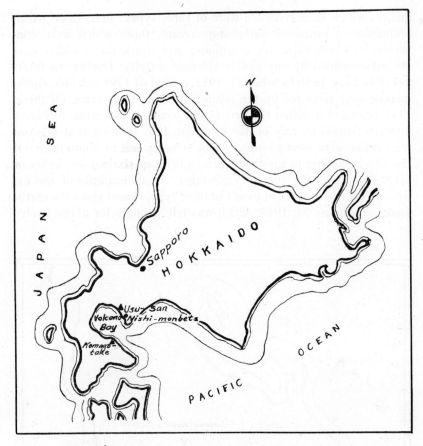

Fig. 76. Detail map of Hokkaido and Usu-San volcano.

Asama-yama

This volcano is situated in the central part of the main island of Japan eighty-five miles northwest of Tokyo. It was in more or less continuous eruption[36] during the years 1909–1914. Between the years 1911 and 1916 seismographs were operated during the summer months at Yuno-taira high on the flanks of the mountain and less than a mile and a half from the center of the crater. During the winter these seismographs were operated at Ashino-taira three miles horizontally distant from the center of the crater, but 1800 feet lower down, near the base of the mountain. The volcanic earthquakes which were recorded were of three types: first, those which accompanied explosive outbursts; second, those which were connected with non-explosive eruptions; and third, those which were not accompanied by any visible volcanic activity. During the interval from May 16 to October 31, 1912, a total of 1798 volcanic earthquakes were recorded by the seismographs at Yuno-taira. Of these, 1111 belonged to either the first or the second class; while 687 were unaccompanied by any visible eruption. It is striking that none of the former were strong enough to be sensibly felt at Yuno-taira. Of the 687 belonging to the third class, a little more than one in six or a total of 124 were felt at Yuno-taira. As an example of the extremely local character of even the third type, Omori gives the earthquake of August 24, 1913, which was felt strongly for about twelve

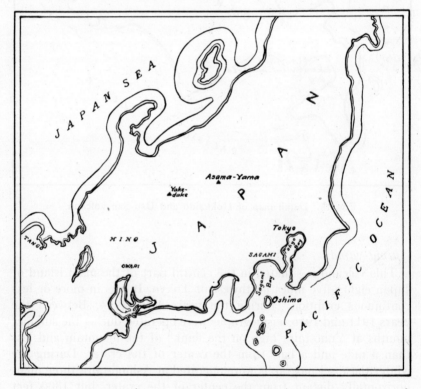

Fig. 77. Map of central Japan showing the location of Asama-Yama volcano.

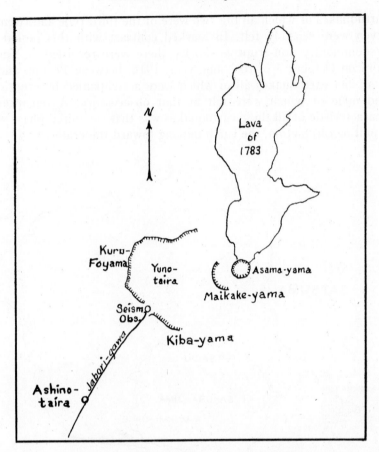

Fig. 78. Sketch of Asama-Yama and vicinity.

seconds at Yuno-taira, but was barely perceptible at Ashino-taira a mile and a half farther away and was not felt at all at Komoro at the southwest base of the mountain. One of the strongest of the earthquakes recorded during the interval mentioned was that of July 16, 1912. It belonged to the third type and was well recorded at Nagano and Maebashi and even at Tokyo eighty-four miles distant. Its origin, according to Omori, was in the Asama-yama mountain mass a little to the west of the central cone. During the hours that followed, from forty-five minutes, and sixteen seconds after seven o'clock a.m., when this earthquake occurred, until ten o'clock the same morning, there were recorded at Yuno-taira 165 earthquakes of which all but two were of the third type and twenty-seven were sensibly felt. In marked contrast with this period of predominantly non-eruptive shocks, there were recorded at Yuno-taira on October 2 of the same year, 1912, between 11 a.m. and 6 a.m., 244 earthquakes all of which were accompanied by eruptions and none of which were felt at that observatory. A remarkable characteristic of all these earthquakes was that the initial phase was a pull or rarefaction, the earth moving toward the crater.

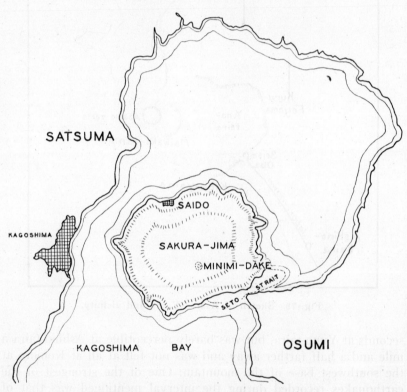

Fig. 79. Detail map of Sakura-Jima.

Sakura-jima

One of the greatest eruptions[37] of modern times was the comparatively sudden outbreak of the volcano Sakura-jima in Kagoshima Bay at the southern tip of the island of Kyushu, Japan, in January, 1914. About 3:41 a.m., January 11, the inhabitants of the city of

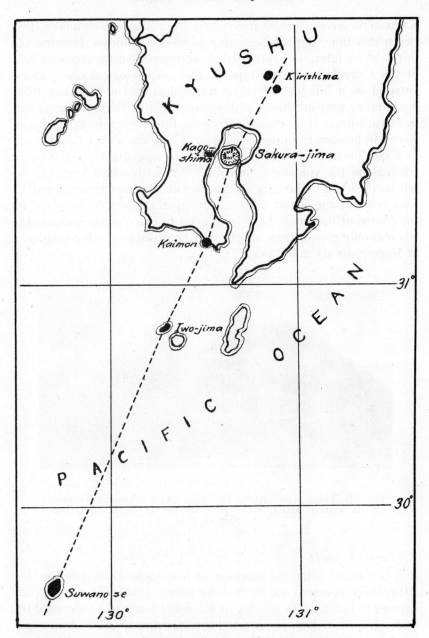

Fig. 80. Location of Sakura-Jima with reference to other volcanoes
of Southern Japan.

Kagoshima were aroused from sleep by a sharp earthquake. Between this time and the beginning of the eruption on January 12, thirty hours later, 418 earthquakes were recorded by seismographs of the Gray-Milne-Ewing type at the meteorological observatory situated on a hill just north of Kagoshima and a little less than seven miles west-northwest of the center of the Minamidake crater in Sakura-jima. How exceedingly local these volcanic earthquakes were will be seen from the fact that 196 of them were not felt at all in Kagoshima and 193 of the others were only slightly perceptible, whereas on the volcanic island itself the earthquakes began to be felt on the night of January 10. In the village of Saido on the northwest coast of the island sixty-six earthquakes were actually felt in the course of the single hour from noon to one o'clock January 11, whereas only nine of these shocks were recorded on the seismographs at Kagoshima six miles away.

— Photo by Lt. W. I. Leahy. Courtesy U. S. Navy

Fig. 81. The volcanic island Iwo-Jima and a submarine eruption off its eastern shore, observed from the U. S. S. *Gold Star*, October 14, 1934.

Tectonic Aspects

A few hours after the eruption of Sakura-jima, on January 12, 1914, there occurred an earthquake strong enough to cause great damage to buildings in the city of Kagoshima and to be recorded by seismographs in Europe. A few hours previously this volcano had burst into violent eruption. A month later another volcano, Iwo-jima, of the same chain as Sakura-jima but situated sixty miles farther south was in eruption and another earthquake occurred in its neighborhood February 13. On November 18, 1913, only two months before the outbreak of Sakura-jima still another volcano of the chain, Mount Kirishima, twenty-eight miles to the north had erupted. It would seem that regional stresses were increasing along the whole chain and were probably responsible for both volcanic and seismic phenomena.[38]

In the preceding chapter, the earthquake of April 2, 1868, in Hawaii was discussed. It was thought by Wood[39] to belong, with many others[40] in those islands, to the tectonic class whose cause is a regional strain responsible for both the volcanic and seismic phenomena, rather than to the strictly volcanic class due to the volcanic processes themselves.

Another case similar to that of Sakura-jima and Hawaii is the Katmai[41] eruption in 1912. The volcano Mount Katmai is situated in the Aleutian Range near the northeastern end of the Aleutian Peninsula on the shores of Shelikof Strait. It had long been dormant when, without such warning as would cause alarm, on the morning of June 6, 1912, it broke into explosive eruption, the sound of which was heard as far as Juneau in southern Alaska, 750 miles away. Immense volumes of volcanic ash were thrown into the atmosphere burying the surroundings of the volcano under ash four feet thick and spreading a layer of fine dust as far south as Juneau and Sitka and as far north as the Yukon valley. All through the three days from June 6 to June 8 its explosive activity continued. Griggs estimated the total quantity of ash and pumice at five cubic miles. During this time and the following days many slight earthquakes were felt. But there were at least four shocks of such magnitude as to be felt at a considerable distance and to be recorded on seismographs in Europe. Tams[42] says of these earthquakes:

> As regards the primary cause, it would be difficult to decide in this case how much was due to tectonic and how much to volcanic-magmatic processes. Hence one must be satisfied to characterize the earthquakes of 1912 in the Katmai region as combined tectonic and magmatic in Branca's sense of the term, and to see in them a particularly striking modern example of the union of tectonic and volcanic phenomena on a grand scale.

Branca[43] divided all earthquakes into three categories: a purely magmatic type, a combined magmatic and tectonic type, and a purely tectonic type; but he assigned far too great importance to the first class.

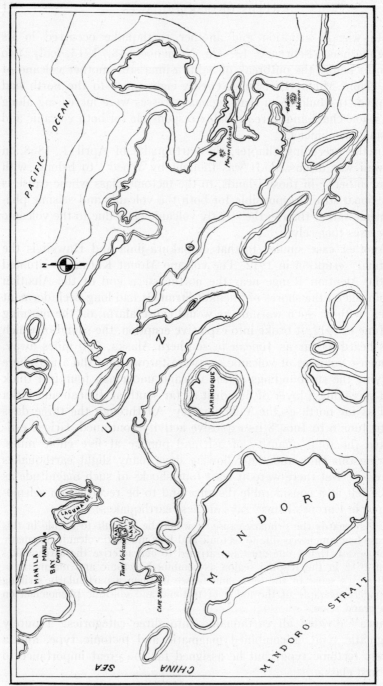

Fig. 82. Volcanoes in the Philippine Islands.

Slight local earthquakes accompanied the eruption of *Bulusan Volcano*[44] in the southeastern part of the island of Luzon in 1916 and 1918 and in the many eruptions of succeeding years which were recorded by a seismograph installed at Irosin, five miles south of the mountain. But these earthquakes were not felt even at that short distance. On the other hand the eruption of the Taal Volcano[45] in southern Luzon in 1911 was accompanied by many stronger earthquakes. During the eruptive period between January 27 and February 7, 1911, 995 shocks were recorded by the seismographs in the Manila Observatory. Of these, at least a few seem to have been of strictly tectonic character; for, although Manila is situated at a distance of thirty-nine miles from the volcano, several of these earthquakes reached an intensity of IV to V Rossi-Forel and were felt up to a distance of 75 to 125 miles. They were recorded by seismographs at Taihoku on the island of Formosa at a distance of more than six hundred miles.

Conclusion

It seems reasonable to infer from the examples quoted that earthquakes caused by volcanic action form a very numerous class, but a relatively unimportant one from the standpoint of the area over which they are felt, the extent of the damage done, or the total energy radiated by them. On the other hand, a common tectonic cause which stores up regional strain energy seems to be ultimately responsible, at times, for both volcanic and seismic phenomena on a large scale, so that truly tectonic earthquakes of considerable magnitude may accompany volcanic eruption and volcanic earthquake shocks. It has been suggested by some that regional strain may *normally* have much to do with volcanic activity.

PLUTONIC OR DEEP FOCUS EARTHQUAKES

The earthquakes which have been considered thus far originated in the outer shell or crust of the earth. The point at which faulting or fracture started and from which the first elastic vibrations in the earthquake were propagated is called the focus. In volcanic earthquakes the depth of the focus is very slight, many shocks starting from a point in the mountain mass which is actually higher than the surrounding country. In tectonic earthquakes the depth of focus is greater, amounting usually to several miles at least. As stated in the

preceding chapter, Hodgson[46] found that the depth of focus of the Tango earthquake was of the order of twelve kilometers (7.5 miles). The foci of the aftershocks of that earthquake were mostly of lesser depth.

On the other hand, earthquakes do occur which have originated at depths measurable in hundreds of kilometers. The hypothesis of deep-focus earthquakes was strongly urged by Turner.[47] Oldham[48] was led by the observations of Turner and by the calculations of Pilgrim,[49] which latter were largely based on mistaken assumptions, to postulate that tectonic earthquakes have a double character which he compared to the firing of a shell from a cannon and the later detonation of the shell. The first he called the "bathyseism" which is, he said, caused by a sudden change of volume due to recrystallization at a depth of several hundred kilometers and which, according to him, constitutes the source of the elastic waves which are recorded by distant seismographs. The second phenomenon he called the "episeism." It consists of the faulting which may be visible at the surface and of the sensible vibrations which do the damage and to which he wished to restrict the name *earthquake*. He thought such

— Courtesy Manila Observatory

Fig. 83. The crater of Taal volcano.

a distinction necessary, for example, to explain the existence of secondary areas of high intensity in the California earthquake of April 18, 1906,[50] and in the Assam earthquake of June 12, 1897. However, while seismologists saw no inherent impossibility in the type of disturbance postulated by Oldham as a "bathyseism," they could not accept the simultaneous existence of his "bathyseism" and "episeism" because the elastic energy which is released in what he called the "episeism" when it is observed, as was the case in most of the earthquakes described in the preceding chapter, is quite sufficient to account for the earthquake waves that are recorded by seismographs. Hence there should have been recorded two distinct suites of wave trains traveling by slightly different paths from the two foci. But that is not the case. G. W. Walker,[51] misled by erroneous assumptions in regard to crustal structure, believed that the high angle at which seismic rays are observed to emerge at the surface of the earth could only be explained on the basis of focal depths ranging from one-sixth to one-fifth of the earth's radius.

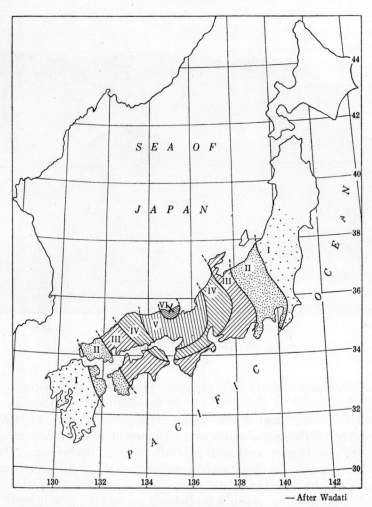

— After Wadati

Fig. 84. Distribution of surface intensities in the normal North Tazima earthquake.

While his conclusions rested on false premises, he deserves credit for developing the important idea that there will be two paths by which a seismic ray can reach a distant point after a single reflection at the earth's surface if the focus is at finite depth. One possible point of reflection will be near the middle of the path and the other near the origin. This fact was used by Stechschulte[52] in his study of the deep Japanese earthquake of March 29, 1928, by which he

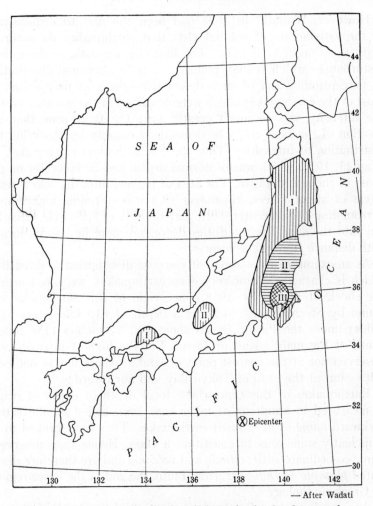

— After Wadati

Fig. 85. Abnormal distribution of intensity in the deep earthquake of March 29, 1928.

showed that it originated at a depth of approximately 255 miles.
The double point of reflection was also used by Scrase[53] to identify
several deep earthquakes and to determine their order of depth.
This he did by assuming a depth of focus, applying the observations
of Turner to the trajectories calculated by Knott and then compar-
ing these calculations with the observed arrival times of various
waves.

However, Wadati[54] in 1928 had been the first to demonstrate to the satisfaction of seismologists that earthquakes do occur at depths of hundreds of miles. The first characteristic of these deep disturbances which Wadati pointed out is an abnormal distribution of perceptibility and of such destructive effects as may occur. In most of the earthquakes which were described in the second chapter, the intensity was so much greater near the fault zone that the position of the fault could be determined roughly by observing the distribution of intensities. Thus the North Tazima earthquake[55] of May 23, 1925, which was of normal depth, had its epicenter on the coast of the sea of Japan. The area of highest intensity was a semi-circle of about fifteen kilometers (9.3 miles) radius immediately surrounding the epicenter, such that the rest of the circle extended out into the sea. The intensities decreased more or less uniformly with distance from this epicenter.

As an example of the apparently erratic distribution of intensities which is characteristic of very deep earthquakes, we may consider the shock of March 29, 1928. The origin of this earthquake was found by Stechschulte[56] to lie at a depth of 410 kilometers (254 miles) under the Pacific Ocean about 300 kilometers (186 miles) south of the main island of Japan. Yet the highest intensity was observed not at the nearest point of land — where it was not even felt — but at the head of Tokyo Bay and northward.

Earthquakes of this type whose focal depth or depth of origin is measured in hundreds of miles have been called by the rather awkward name of *deep-focus* earthquakes. They have proved to be sufficiently numerous to constitute a class. Hence they deserve a name co-ordinate with *tectonic* and *volcanic* and are therefore designated *plutonic earthquakes,* from Pluto, the god of the lower regions in Greek mythology.

An ingenious chart for the determination of the depth of plutonic earthquakes has been devised by the Reverend George J. Brunner, S.J., at St. Louis University. It is published by John Wiley and Sons under the title *Brunner Depth-Time-Distance Chart* and is based on timed arrivals of direct and reflected waves.

Chapter IV

WHY EARTHQUAKES?

It is reliably estimated that more than a million earthquakes, weak and strong, occur somewhere every year. That is more than twenty-seven hundred a day! And there is plenty of evidence to show that this is no new condition. It has been going on for ages. Why?

When we consider the geological processes that have been and are now at work refashioning our globe, we are struck by two generalizations. First the *original attitude* of the layers of sand and mud and limey ooze, whose consolidation made the stratified sediments under our feet, must have been a *horizontal* one. Sediment sinks down and spreads out as flat as possible under the action of gravity. Second, sediments are moved along gradually downgrade and finally come to rest in the oceans where the remains of myriads of marine organisms settle upon them and mix with them and become fossilized as a part of them. Thus *marine strata* predominate among the sedimentary rocks of the earth and they may be recognized as such through the *marine fossils* they contain.

Therefore, if we find marine sediments in the interior of the continents, high above sea level, and furthermore, if we find them tilted up, or folded into mountain chains, or driven over each other on thrust planes, as we actually do, we conclude at once to the operation of giant forces which have elevated them and compressed them laterally. Mountain building forces are called by geologists *orogenic;* and those which raise up the continents, or considerable parts of them, are called *epeirogenic* forces.

Our experience with the earthquakes of the present leads us to link them up in some fashion with the geological processes of the present and the past, and in particular with orogenic and epeirogenic phenomena.

When we speak of the causes of earthquakes we must distinguish clearly between three things: first, those causes which are really

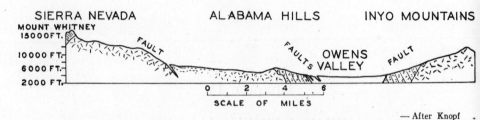

— After Knopf

Fig. 86. Diagrammatic section across the Owens Valley, California.

responsible for storing up the terrible energy released at the time of an earthquake; second, the mechanism by which that energy is released; and third, the trigger forces which merely determine that an earthquake which is about to occur should happen today rather than tomorrow, at this particular instant rather than later. A trigger does not load a gun. Neither does its force propel the bullet. Pulling the trigger merely determines when the charge already in the gun shall explode and send the bullet on its way. So it is with the trigger forces of earthquakes. We shall treat of these three types of causes separately.

EVIDENCE FROM GEOLOGY

As a basis for the discussion of the primary causes of earthquakes let us consider the geological conditions in a few typical places where earthquakes have occurred.

— Photo by Rev. W. C. Repetti, S.J.

Fig. 87. Road built over earthquake fault scarp in Owens Valley. Looking north near Lone Pine, California. Inyo Range in the right background.

Grabens

For example, Figure 86 shows a diagrammatic section after Knopf[57] from the crest of the Sierra Nevada to the crest of the Inyo Range across the Owens Valley where, as we have seen in the second chapter, a violent earthquake occurred on March 26, 1872. The alluviated Owens Valley lies between the lofty Inyo Range (Fig. 87) on the east and the Alabama Hills on the west with the Sierra Nevada towering beyond the latter (Fig. 88). The earthquake of 1872 occurred on a system of faults which formed along the eastern base of the Alabama Hills. These hills are but a detail in the general faulting of the valley. All of the geological evidence indicates that Owens Valley is a trough or *graben* whose floor has subsided relatively along two more or less parallel fault zones, the one at the base of the Sierra Nevada, the other at the base of the Inyo Range.

— Photo by Rev. James B. Macelwane, S.J.

Fig. 88. Looking west in the Owens Valley near Lone Pine, California. In the foreground is a recent fault scarp on which movement occurred in the earthquake of March 26, 1872. In the middle ground are the Alabama Hills bounded by an older fault. In the background rises the lofty front of the Sierra Nevada, its crest culminating in Mount Whitney at the left of the center.

Rifts

Another prolific source of earthquakes will be found in those structural features called *rift valleys* or simply *rifts*. *Rift valleys* are structural depressions, linear in character, which are produced along fault zones. A zone may be so intricately faulted on a large scale as to crush the rocks within it and reduce them largely to gouge and breccia. They will then be so much less resistant to weathering than

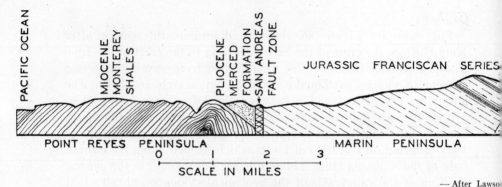

Fig. 89. Diagrammatic NE-SW section across the San Andreas
Fault Zone near Bolinas, California.

the firm rocks on either side of the zone that a depression will soon
be created. Figure 89, for example, presents a geological section
after Lawson[58] across the rift in which the fault trace appeared in the
California earthquake of April 18, 1906. This cross section follows
a line from the Pacific Ocean on the west side of the Point Reyes
Peninsula in an east-northeasterly direction past the northern end
of Bolinas Lagoon into the highlands of the Marin Peninsula. The

— Courtesy Carnegie Inst. of Washington

Fig. 90. The fault trace of the earthquake of April 18, 1906, passing
into San Andreas Lake in the San Andreas Rift Valley, California.

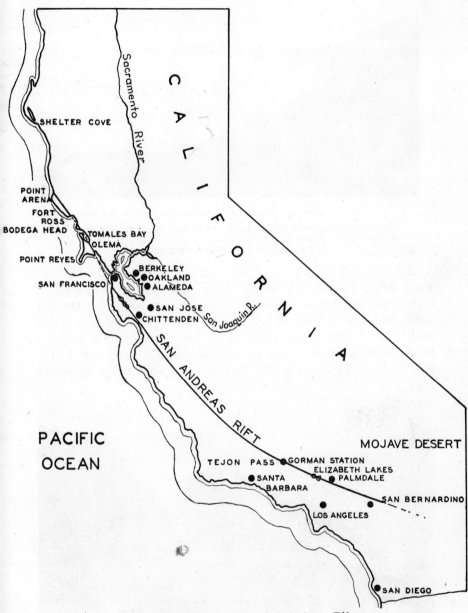

Fig. 91. Sketch map of the San Andreas Rift.

— Photo by A. C. Lawson. Courtesy Univ. of California

Fig. 92. San Andreas Rift passing out to sea two miles southeast of Fort Ross. Trace of the earthquake fault of April 18, 1906, in the foreground. Looking southeast.

Point Reyes Peninsula is distinct both geographically and geologically from the Marin Peninsula. They are separated by the rift valley which is both an old belt of dislocation, and a recently active fault zone. Although this valley is marked by typical rift features throughout its length, these features are so well developed in the San Andreas Valley (Fig. 90) farther south on the San Francisco

— Photo by Rev. James B. Macelwane, S.J.

Fig. 93. Looking northwest up Tomales Bay in the San Andreas Rift.

— Photo by Rev. James B. Macelwane, S.J.

Fig. 94. Looking southeast down the San Andreas Rift near the head of Bolinas Lagoon.

Peninsula that this striking depression has received the name San Andreas Rift. The correct Spanish name would be, of course, *San Andrés*, but the curious American corruption San Andreas has be-

— Photo by Rev. James B. Macelwane, S.J.

Fig. 95. The San Andreas Rift entering the San Francisco peninsula from the sea at Mussel Rock. A huge landslide took place here during the great earthquake of April 18, 1906.

— Photo by H. W. Fairbanks. Courtesy Carnegie Inst. of Washington
Fig. 96. Lower Lake Elizabeth in the San Andreas Rift.

come so rooted in the literature that it will probably be retained. The San Andreas Rift is one of the major tectonic lines of California. Its genesis goes back at least to Pliocene time. Many destructive earthquakes are known historically to have occurred on it. Two of the greatest were the earthquake of 1906 which involved the northern part of the Rift and that of 1857 which involved the middle and southern parts.

The San Andreas Rift may be traced for a distance of more than 500 miles (Fig. 91) except for short intervals where it is under the sea (Fig. 92). The portion which lies between the Point Reyes Peninsula and the Marin Peninsula is occupied for many miles at its northern end by Tomales Bay and at its southern end by Bolinas Lagoon and Bay. The trace of the earthquake fault of 1906 could

— Photo by H. W. Fairbanks. Courtesy Univ. of California
**Fig. 97. Alkali flat in the San Andreas Rift near Job's Ranch south
of Carissa Plains.**

— Photo by H. W. Fairbanks. Courtesy Univ. of California

Fig. 98. Looking along the San Andreas Rift past Gorman Station from a point a little below Tejon Pass. Note the irregular, hummocky floor of the rift valley.

be readily followed from the one to the other (Figs. 93 and 94). Passing under the sea outside the Golden Gate the San Andreas Rift enters the San Francisco Peninsula at Mussel Rock (Fig. 95). Beyond Chittenden Pass the rift traverses mountainous country then enters Carissa Plains, crosses Tejon Pass, skirts the Mojave Desert and the northern slope of the San Gabriel Mountains, crosses Cajon Pass to the southern flank of the San Bernardino Mountains, and is finally lost in the Colorado Desert. Throughout most of its length the rift forms a well-defined series of valleys, few of which are occupied by streams of any importance. The rift features occupy a belt from one-half to one mile wide characterized by low ridges parallel to the general axis of the depression with intervening ravines. Its floor is everywhere hummocky and marked by ponds or alkali flats, ridges, sags, and fault scarps (Figs. 96 to 99). Its geology is exceedingly complex, consisting largely of slivers in a matrix of fault breccia or gouge, and showing evidence of relative displace-

— Photo by H. W. Fairbanks. Courtesy Univ. of California

Fig. 99. Looking southeast down Lone Pine Canyon toward Cajon Pass and the San Bernardino Mountains.

— Photo by Rev. James B. Macelwane, S.J.

Fig. 100. Temescal Valley, a part of the Haywards Rift. Berkeley Hills west of Claremont, California.

Fig. 101. Haywards Rift west of Lake Chabot near Oakland,
California.

ments of thousands of feet both in a vertical sense and in a horizontal direction parallel to the rift.

Parallel to the San Andreas Rift on the east side of San Francisco
Bay close to the western face of the Berkeley Hills, runs the Haywards Rift (Figs. 100 and 101). It was in this rift that the fault
trace appeared in the destructive Haywards earthquake of October
21, 1868. Figure 102 shows the geographical relationships of the two
rifts. As in the case of the San Andreas Rift, the Haywards Rift
bears unmistakable evidence of vertical and horizontal displacements of considerable extent.

Thrust Zones

We may take as a third example of the geology of an earthquake
zone the "great boundary fault" around the southern face of the
Himalaya Mountains which we mentioned in Chapter II when de-
scribing the Kangra earthquake. Between the Indo-Gangetic plain
and the steep slopes of the snowy ranges which are composed of
schists, limestones, quartzites, and slates of the older Himalayan
series, there rise the foothill ridges of Tertiary sandstones, conglomerates and shales which belong to the Siwalik system. The very old
Himalayan rocks of the higher mountains have been thrust over the
lower Siwaliks and these again over the middle and upper Siwaliks

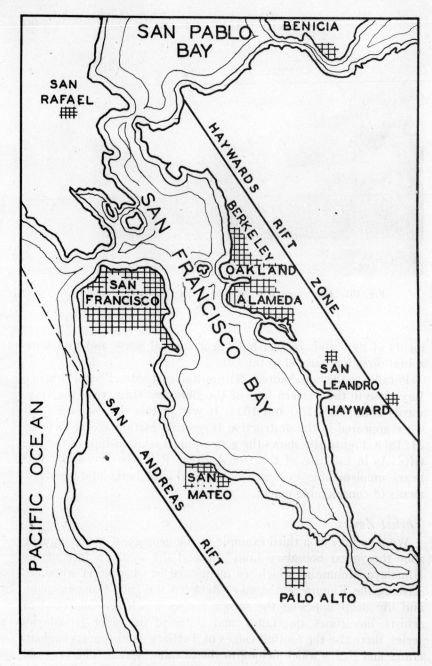

Fig. 102. Relation of the Haywards Rift to the San Andreas Rift in San Francisco Bay region.

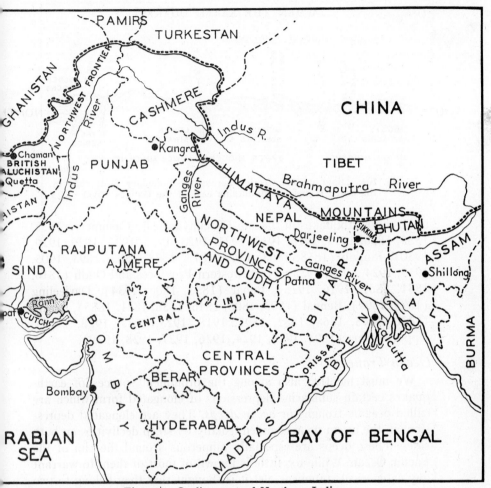

Fig. 103. Outline map of Northern India.

in what is known as the Great Boundary Fault zone of the Himalayas. From the vale of Cashmere on the west, all the way around past the Indo-Gangetic plain on the southwest and south to the hills of Assam and upper Burma on the east, the towering mass of the central Himalayas seems to be pressing forward bit by bit crumpling and overriding the plains of India. The story of this tremendous effort seems to be written in the history of earthquakes in northern India. Since about the middle of the nineteenth century when satisfactory records were begun, the number of destructive earthquakes that have occurred first at one point and then at another around this boundary fault zone is appalling. The following is a partial list

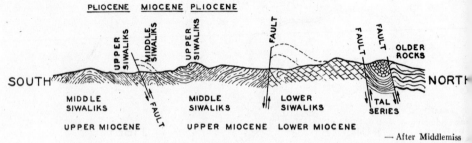

— After Middlemiss

Fig. 104. Diagrammatic section across the boundary fault zone in
the outer Himalaya Mountains east of the Ganges River.

of strong earthquakes in the sub-Himalayan belt: Cashmere (1828, 1885, 1886, 1914, 1916, 1917, 1921, 1923, 1926, 1927, 1928, 1929, 1930), Punjab (1858, 1868, 1869, 1875, 1878, 1883, 1893, 1905, 1919, 1924, 1929, 1930), Northwestern Provinces and Oudh (1816, 1831, 1861, 1916, 1925), Behar (1833, 1866, 1934), Darjeeling (1875, 1899), Bengal (1803, 1808, 1846, 1856, 1881, 1885), Assam (1830, 1845, 1868, 1882, 1897, 1918, 1923, 1927, 1928, 1930), Upper Burma (1894, 1918, 1924, 1926, 1927, 1928, 1929).

Ocean Troughs

We must mention also among the prominent sources of earthquakes certain submarine depressions of elongated form which are called oceanic troughs or *ocean deeps*. They are elongated depressions in the ocean floor bounded usually by steep declivities on both sides. These deeps are especially numerous around the rim of the Pacific Ocean. While too little is known of most of them to warrant any categorical statement, yet it is thought that they belong to two distinct types. The one type according to Vening-Meinesz is a downfold of the crust into the substratum as a result of downward convection currents. This type of deep is characterized by large negative gravity anomalies indicating a deficiency of mass. This deficiency is interpreted as due to the substitution of the light crustal rocks for the heavier substratum which is pushed downward and out of the way. Earthquakes do not occur in the trough or on the flanks of this type of deep but at some distance to one side. Examples of this kind of deep are the Brownson trough north of Puerto Rico in the West Indies and the deep in the East Indies south of Java and Sumatra.

The second kind of deep is characterized by positive gravity anomalies indicating excess mass and may be exemplified by the Bartlett Trough (Fig. 105) which extends from the Gulf of Honduras on the west, passing between Swan Island and the Caymans and between Jamaica and the south coast of Cuba, to the western end of the Island of Hispaniola on the east. The declivities are quite steep especially near the eastern end and seem to have the characteristics of active fault scarps. The southern face of the Sierra Maestra near Santiago de Cuba is undoubtedly a fault scarp according to Taber. Both Taber and Hess agree that the floor of the Bartlett Trough near the east end is a jumble of down faulted blocks. The trough, therefore, would seem to be a submarine *graben*. Violent earthquakes occur quite frequently along its flanks especially in Cuba and Jamaica.

Off the western coast of South America are the Atacama and Peruvian deeps. Soundings up to a depth of 6400 meters (3500 fathoms) were taken in the Guatamalan Deep, on the Pacific coast of Central America. South of Mexico is the Acapulco Deep on which a long series of earthquakes have recently occurred which caused great damage in Oaxaca and in the neighboring Mexican states. The Aleutian Deep, south of the western part of the Aleutian Peninsula and of the eastern Aleutian Islands is a perennial source of strong earthquakes. The Kurile Island Deep, the Tuscarora Deep east of

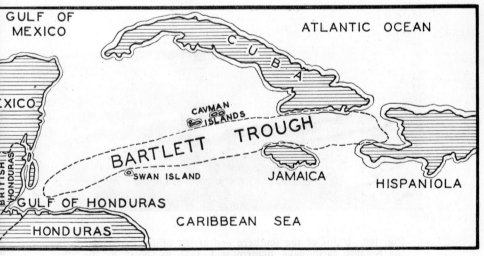

Fig. 105. Bartlett Trough.

Japan, the Riu-Kiu, and the Philippine deeps east of the islands of those names complete the Pacific border series. Other important depressions in the western Pacific Ocean are the Paula, Yap, and Guam deeps near those islands and the Kermadec and Tonga deeps between New Zealand and Samoa.

Faulting and Warping

We have given, it is true, but a few examples of the geologic structures of regions subject to earthquakes. However, these examples were chosen for their clearness and in the belief that they represent typical cases. One fact seems to emerge from them all: some earthquakes are connected with faults.

On the other hand, we must not lose sight of two facts. First, the earthquakes that are actually accompanied by the production of visible fault traces or fault scarps on the surface of the earth are a small minority of the world's earthquakes. Second, a fault cannot become visible unless it comes up to the surface and unless the relative displacement on it is sufficient to be measurable. A considerable movement on a low-angle fault deep down in the earth might produce *warping* that could be detected. In fact, such changes of ground level in an earthquake have often been measured, as in the case of the Assam, Messina, Kwanto, and Yakutat Bay earthquakes. But for every earthquake that is violent enough and has its origin suffi-

— Photo by M. Matsuyama

Fig. 106. Uplift of the southern end of the Miura Peninsula during the Kwanto earthquake, September 1, 1923, as shown by the white band of dead marine organisms.

Fig. 107. Uplift of the west side of Disenchantment Bay, Alaska, in the Yakutat Bay earthquakes of September, 1899. The amount of actual elevation indicated by the distance between the old shore line and the present sea level is 14.4 meters (47 feet and 4 inches).

Fig. 108. Forest at the north end of Khantaak Island killed by submergence in the Yakutat Bay earthquakes of September, 1899.

ciently near to the surface to be accompanied by any visible faulting or warping, there are millions of earthquakes that have no measurable surface expression. What then is the ultimate cause of the faulting and of earthquakes in general?

ULTIMATE CAUSES

Why should earthquakes occur at all? Every earthquake releases energy that is radiated in the form of vibrations or earthquake waves. What is the source of that energy? Apparently the rocks were overstrained to such an extent that they gave way by fracture or faulting. What strained them? We really do not know. We say the strains are produced by the forces that cause continental uplift and mountain building — *epeirogenic* and *orogenic* forces. But what are these forces and what is their origin? We here enter the realm of speculation. Leet[59] well remarks in this connection: "Human curiosity makes it practically impossible to refrain from occasional attempts to fit the accumulating facts of observation into a general theory of the forces back of it all. Such rationalizing hypotheses are essential to any science. They supply valuable stimuli and guide programs of investigation. Their greatest danger has often been their tendency to induce a slurring of the boundaries between fact and hypothesis."

Some of the suggestions that have been made as to the ultimate causes of earthquakes are the following.

Shortening of the Earth's Crust by Cooling and Contraction

It is assumed in this theory that the earth was formed in a molten or gaseous state and that it cooled down gradually by processes of radiation, conduction, and convection until a crust was formed. As the cooling and consequent shrinkage continued beneath the crust, the latter would be always too large and would therefore wrinkle and collapse by folding and faulting along zones of weakness. Aside from the fact that this is but one hypothesis for the origin of the earth, serious doubts have been raised, first because of the fact that no remnant of the supposed original crust has ever been found; and second because no reasonable supposition as to crustal strength would explain the supposed transmission of compressional forces over the hundreds and even thousands of miles that intervene in some cases between the geosynclines or zones filled with weak sediments where the folding and faulting has taken place; and finally because we do not know the vertical distribution of radioactive minerals in the earth which are evolving heat and which, if present in proper quantities, would be quite sufficient to account for the observed temperature increase with depth in the earth's crust. In fact Jeffreys has calculated that there would be *too much heat* if these minerals continued to greater depths in the same proportions as found near the surface.

Isostasy

The word isostasy is derived from the Greek ἴσος equal and ἵστημι I balance (isos + stasis), and means a condition of balance — hydrostatic balance, if you will — between adjacent segments of the earth's crust. If we take two columns of equal cross section and equal height, the one will weigh more than the other if it is composed of heavier, that is, of denser material. Again if two columns of equal cross section are composed of the same or equally dense material the one which is the longer will weigh the more. Applying this to the earth's crust, a column from the top of Mount Everest down to say seventy miles below sea level is surely longer than one from the plain of the Ganges in Northern India to the same depth below sea level. Therefore, if both columns are taken of equal cross section and if they were composed of the same kind of rock the Himalayan column would weigh more than the Gangetic column. Now the scientists of the Geodetic Survey of India, measuring the relative weights by a deflection of a pendulum, found that the towering masses of the Himalaya Mountains did not attract a pendulum in proportion to their height above the Gangetic plain. The Indian scientists therefore concluded that there is lighter rock material under the mountains than under the plain. In fact there seemed to be just enough heavy rock under the Gangetic plain and light rock under the Himalaya Mountains to balance them against each other. In the course of time there came to be two main theories as to how these two and all other similar areas were balanced.

According to Airy's hypothesis the lighter mass of the Himalayas floats like an iceberg in the denser substratum. Therefore, as in the case of the iceberg, the greater part of the Himalayas is below the surface (Fig. 109). Hence, Airy's conception came to be called the "roots of the mountains theory." Pratt's hypothesis, on the other

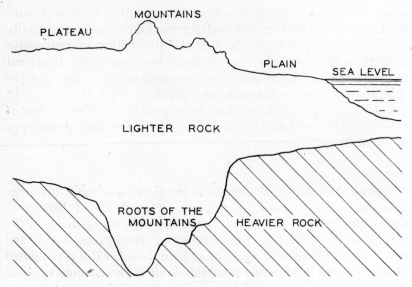

Fig. 109. Isostasy according to the Airy hypothesis.

hand, assumed that there is some level, the same the world over, at which all columns are in complete balance, that is, differences in height are exactly balanced out by differences in the density of the materials composing these colums (Figs. 110 and 111).

Now what has this to do with the causes of earthquakes? A static condition never exists for long on the earth. Geological processes are at work. Weathering and erosion are shortening the mountain columns. The eroded rock fragments are carried down by streams and deposited on top of the shorter columns thus lengthening them. Therefore, the balance tends to be forever disturbed by geological wear on the different mountain ranges. The balance between columns could not everywhere exist unless there is some mechanism of compensation whereby heavier material down in the interior of the crust is removed from the columns that are receiving the load and added to the columns that are being eroded away. The rock is solid. Hence, if such a transfer occurs it must take place by rock *flowage* as cold steel is made to flow in the die. One can readily see what tremendous force the moving rock mass must exert on the surrounding material that is continuous with it and how easily the overlying rocks may be folded and faulted.

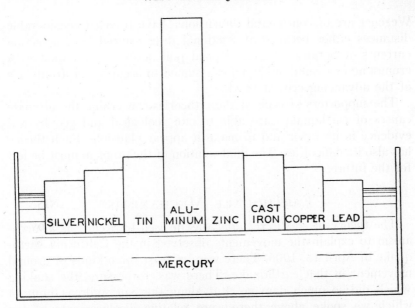

Fig. 110. Simple isostatic equilibrium. Equal masses of lighter metals of the same cross section will float on mercury with their bases in the same plane and their tops irregular.

The *thermal cycle theory* assumes that radioactive minerals are present throughout the crust to at least the same extent as they are observed at the surface. More heat is generated locally than can be conducted away. Expansion takes place. Rocks are overstrained and eventually yield by folding and faulting.

The *migration theory* supposes that blocks, which according to

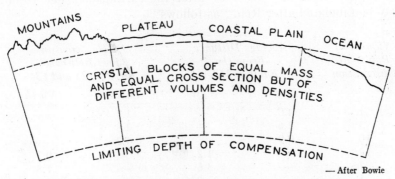

— After Bowie

Fig. 111. Isostasy according to the Pratt hypothesis.

Wegener are of continental dimensions, have traveled considerable distances either because of frictional drag exerted by convection currents or because of gravitational pull down a slight incline. A crumpling of mountain chains is assumed to occur at the front face of the advancing crustal block.

The supporters of each of these theories concerning the ultimate causes of earthquakes are able to cite geological and geophysical evidence in its favor and to make it appear plausible. Each theory has also its difficulties. The final solution of the problem must be left for the future.

EARTHQUAKE MECHANISMS

The theory of *elastic rebound* was devised by Reid[60] as a mechanism to explain the movements observed in the California earthquake of April 18, 1906. There were at least three kinds of ground movement in that earthquake. There was, to be sure, the shaking which did so much damage. But along the San Andreas fault of which we spoke above there were relative displacements of the ground which gave rise to the shaking and remained permanently visible. Third, there was a regional movement to which the faulting was a reaction and which was revealed only by precise triangulation. The United States Coast and Geodetic Survey had made careful measurements of angles and distances long before the earthquake and were able to repeat the triangulation afterward and thus to determine by comparison the displacements throughout the region.

The surveys may be divided into three groups: First, those made between 1851 and 1866; second, those between 1874 and 1892; third, that made in 1906–1907 after the earthquake. The results may be tabulated after Reid[61] as follows:

Number of Points of Observation	Average Distance From the Fault in Miles		Displacement in Feet Between Surveys (2) and (3)	
	East	West	South	North
1	4.0	—	1.8	—
3	2.6	—	2.8	—
10	0.9	—	4.2	—
12	—	1.2	—	9.7
7	—	3.6	—	7.8
1	—	23.0	—	4.8

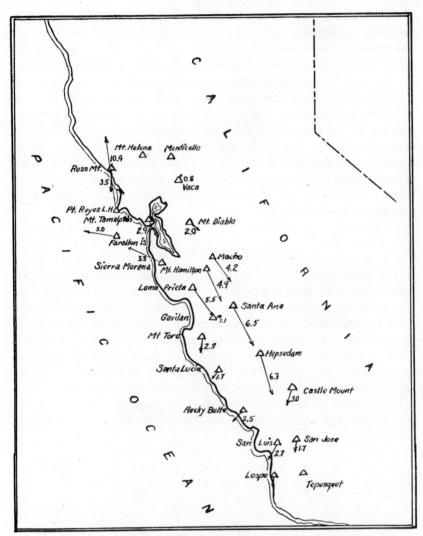

Fig. 112. The amounts and directions of actual movement in the California earthquake of April 18, 1906, are indicated by the arrows.

Thus the displacements decreased rapidly eastward from the fault but seemed to indicate a regional displacement on the west. From these data Reid developed his elastic rebound theory which has been generally accepted. "What kind of forces could have caused this movement? Gravity could not have been the immediate cause of the sudden and nearly horizontal displacements, nor could volcanic explosions; the only forces capable of producing such movements are elastic forces. Since the material composing the earth's crust is elastic, and cannot rupture until it is strained beyond its strength it is evident that an earlier relative displacement of regions on opposite sides of the fault had set up an elastic strain in the intermediate zone which exceeded the strength of the rock, causing the rupture along the fault surface; and that the rock on opposite sides of the fault, under the action of its own elastic stresses, then suddenly sprang back to positions of equilibrium, the opposite sides moving in opposite directions, and relieving the elastic strain. This is the only satisfactory explanation of the observation and determined displacements."[62]

Trigger Forces

The third type of cause is the *trigger force*. Some of the trigger forces that have been suggested are the tidal pull of the moon and sun, daily heating and cooling, tidal loading, rainfall, atmospheric pressure gradients and changes, nutation of the earth, mass movements of the atmosphere, and earthquake waves from distant origins. Under given circumstances, of course, it is possible for any of these to constitute "the last straw," so to speak, which will set off an earthquake just ready to go. Many statistical studies have been made in order to determine the extent of their influence; but up to the present the results of these investigations have been generally inconclusive.

Chapter V

WHEN AND WHERE?

Earthquake Prediction

Will there be a destructive earthquake in Japan this year? When will the next great earthquake occur on the San Andreas Rift? Will my daughter be safe in San Francisco this summer? Will New York or Chicago ever suffer a disastrous earthquake such as that which visited Charleston, South Carolina, in 1886, or the middle Mississippi Valley in 1811? Such are the questions that are frequently put to the seismologist by the press and the public. "You always tell us about the earthquakes after they happen. Why can you not foretell earthquakes as the meteorologist forecasts the weather?"

No seismologist in our present state of knowledge is able to *predict* an earthquake in the sense of stating with scientific certainty that it will occur at a precise time and place. Prediction to be useful must give the approximate intensity and the exact time and place.

There were many who have given out so-called earthquake forecasts. Some of these were charlatans and publicity seekers. Others were monomaniacs with a fixed idea. But a few were very sincere people, generally of limited training, who were unable to assess the inadequacy of the causes they invoked and were deceived by coincidences. Since, as we have seen, thousands of earthquakes are occurring every day, it is quite impossible not to find a verification of one's predictions if time and place and intensity are left sufficiently vague.

Warning Sought in Vain

Scientists have not given up hope of some day discovering a reliable indication of the imminence of an earthquake; but so far their efforts have failed. Leaving aside such popular but totally irrelevant indicators as "earthquake weather," and such phenomena as the positions of the heavenly bodies whose tidal effects could at most

Fig. 113. Tide gauge with its float in a well. Installed at the Manila Observatory in 1888 to study the relation between earthquakes and the height and oscillations of the ground water.

provide trigger forces of very doubtful efficacy, scientists have investigated the possible occurrence of warnings, such as foreshocks too small perhaps to be noticed, the behavior of animals before a shock, rapid tilting of the earth's surface, changes in the flow of springs and of water level in wells, but none of these seems to correlate with earthquakes in such a way as to furnish a reliable indicator.

To be reliable they must never occur when no earthquake follows and should be observable before most if not all shocks. This is not the case. Swarms of very small earthquakes are sometimes observed with suitable instruments; but they usually die out without being followed by any major shock. Very slight tremors sometimes precede the main earthquake which may alarm sensitive animals and may come within the range of human audibility as sounds; but this is not always the case. Nor are such phenomena always followed by a sensible shock when they do occur.

Accumulating Strain

According to the elastic rebound theory an earthquake will occur when the accumulating strain in the rocks reaches the rupturing value. Hence, if it were possible to tell when and how fast rock strain is building up toward this critical value we should be able to predict the earthquake. This cannot be done by direct observation because a rock under strain looks the same as one free from strain. Many scientists hoped, however, that such growth of strain might be detected by instrumental means.

— Photo by B. A. Baird

Fig. 114. View of the southeast and northeast monuments on the east side of the road near Olema. The protecting cap has been propped up for observation of the spindle.

— Photo by B. A. Baird

Fig. 115. Looking east from the northwest monument in the orchard to the northeast monument beyond the fence on the opposite side of the road near Olema, California, showing the transit in place and observations in progress.

— Photo by B. A. Baird

Fig. 116. The southwest monument in the San Andreas
Rift at Crystal Springs Lake with the protecting cap
removed.

Test Pillars

Immediately after the California earthquake of 1906 pillars were
set up on opposite sides of the San Andreas fault trace near Olema
and their relative positions were determined with high precision.
The same was done in the rift near San Andreas Lake. The measurements have been repeated from time to time since then but no relative movement has ever been detected.

— Photo by B. A. Baird

Fig. 117. The northeast monument at Crystal Springs
Lake in the San Andreas Rift.

— Photo by B. A. Baird

Fig. 118. Observing with the transit on the northwest monument at Crystal Springs Lake in the San Andreas Rift.

The California Program

It was objected that these monuments straddling the fault of 1906 were too close together to show anything but an actual slip on the fault plane. Therefore, appropriations were sought and obtained from the United States Congress to investigate from many angles whether the California Coast Ranges were being subjected to increasing regional strain. To this end the older triangulation was repeated and new arcs were surveyed across the San Andreas Rift and other fault zones; lines of precise leveling were run across these fault zones, and the whole was tied in to the general first order triangulation network of the country. All this was done by the United States Coast and Geodetic Survey. Detailed structural studies of the fault zones were made by the United States Geological Survey and by the universities. Tiltmeters were installed on the campus of the University of California at Berkeley. But in all these years, since the start of this comprehensive program in 1921 under the able chairmanship of Doctor Arthur L. Day, and the immediate direction of Mr. Harry O. Wood, no appreciable regional strain has been discovered. Yet earthquakes have been occurring in large numbers in California and some of them, like the Santa Barbara (1925), Long Beach (1933) and Imperial Valley (1940) earth-

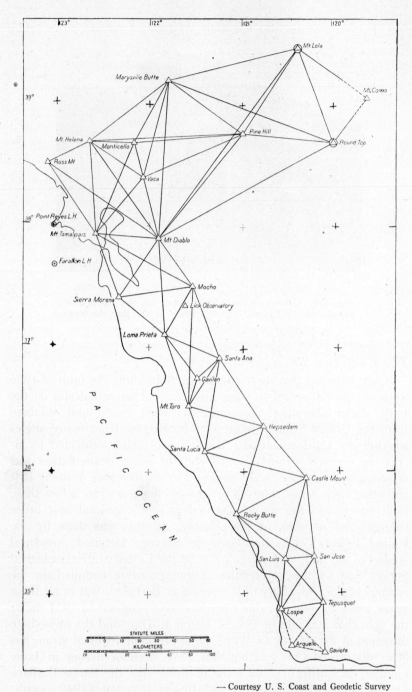

Fig. 119. Map of the 1922 retriangulation of the middle part of the
San Andreas Rift in central California.

quakes were destructive. The information that has been gathered is, of course, very valuable, but it has not led us any nearer to the prediction of earthquakes.

Well-Founded Probabilities

Has all the work of the seismologists, then, during the past several decades been futile? Men of the highest ability and training have been observing and locating earthquakes in all parts of the world. Have they told us nothing whatever about the time and place of occurrence of future earthquakes? Intensive study and careful mapping of the exact location of so many earthquakes has traced a pattern on our globe in which we read with confidence future earthquake probabilities. For example, we know it is much more probable that a destructive earthquake will occur in the neighborhood of Tokyo than in the neighborhood of Chicago. Why? Because the seismological map shows that Tokyo lies on one of the two great earthquake belts on which destructive earthquakes occur very frequently, while Chicago is located in a region where such earthquakes are rare. In fact, if we thumb through the pages of earthquake history we do not find a single instance in which a destructive earthquake centered at Chicago. The nearest to the site of that metropolis was the Aurora earthquake, May 26, 1909, and the nearest catastrophe was the New Madrid earthquake in southeastern Missouri.

Major Earthquake Belts

The more important of the two great earthquake belts of which we have spoken follows the western coast of South America, Central America, and North America, swings westward along the southern coast of Alaska, the Aleutians and the Kurile Islands to Japan, then turns down the east coast of Asia and passes through the Philippine and Solomon Islands to New Zealand; thus forming an almost perfect great circle around the globe. The second belt starts in Mexico, crosses through West Indies to southern Europe, through Asia Minor, India, and the East Indies. A third belt extends down the mid-Atlantic swell from the Arctic Ocean nearly to the Antarctic.

Is Any Place Immune?

In other parts of the world destructive earthquakes occur also, but much less frequently. All of the continental United States[63] and Canada except the western coast[64] lie outside the great earthquake belts; and yet earthquakes have occurred in a great many places and many of these have been strong enough to cause damage and a few have their place among the world's great earthquakes.

Eastern Canada and New England were shaken February 5, 1663, by a famous earthquake which centered in the Saint Lawrence Valley. Another occurred in the same region February 28, 1925, which caused some damage and was felt in Boston, New York, and Detroit. On March 21, 1904, an earthquake occurred near the Atlantic Coast and the Canada-Maine boundary which was strong enough to knock down chimneys. Again on November 1, 1935, a strong earthquake centered near Lake Temiskaming northeast of Georgian Bay. There have been earthquakes also in other parts of Canada even north of Hudson Bay.

On November 18, 1755, a strong earthquake did some damage in Boston. Another earthquake that shook down chimneys and stone walls in Massachusetts occurred November 8, 1727. New York State also has suffered damage from earthquakes as in the case of the Attica shock, August 12, 1929, and the New York Bay earthquake of August 10, 1884. There have been destructive or nearly destructive earthquakes throughout the Appalachian Mountains from Pennsylvania to Georgia, in the Mississippi Valley, in Ohio, Indiana, Michigan, Minnesota, South Dakota, Nebraska, Kansas, Oklahoma, Texas, New Mexico, Colorado, and all the western states. Among the more violent and destructive shocks were the Three Forks (1925) and Helena (1935) earthquakes in Montana, the Elsinore (1921) and Salt Lake (1909, 1934) earthquakes in Utah, and the Pleasant Valley (1915) and Cedar Mountain (1932) earthquakes in Nevada.

Similarly, the British Isles,[65] Northern Europe, Africa, and Australia lie outside the earthquake belts and are stable areas, but are subject to destructive and nearly destructive shocks at less frequent intervals.

In fact there is no place in the world which a prudent seismologist would dare to call totally immune to earthquakes. There is no scientific basis for saying in regard to any locality: "There will never be an earthquake here." The absence of earthquakes on any part of the seismological map tells us at best that none has been recorded from that area in historical times. It says nothing about the geological past, and its only bearing on the earthquakes of the future is the statistical probability it furnishes that they will be rare in that area.

Chapter VI

FIELD STUDY OF EARTHQUAKES

The earthquakes described in the second chapter were accompanied by destructive effects and were felt by human beings. The damage to structures was limited in each to a relatively small area, while the perceptibility of the earthquake extended to a wider region. It is therefore possible not only to compare earthquakes with one another by means of these effects, but to draw many useful conclusions from them.

The Nature of Earthquake Motion

Any person who has gone through the harrowing experience of a violent earthquake knows that it is very difficult indeed to describe the shock except as an utter confusion of blows, jerks, vibrations, and undulations, now in one direction, now in another, up and down and sidewise. How do these movements originate? When a rupture occurs on a fault plane it is quite improbable that it starts simultaneously over a large surface. It probably begins in a very small space where the accumulated elastic stress first reaches the ultimate strength of the rock. The stress being relieved there by the break concentrates on the points near by. These in turn give way and the rupture spreads by very irregular steps. Each sudden start and stop gives rise to vibrations. The chattering of the slipping surfaces due to their roughness and the friction between them causes the rock masses on the two sides to vibrate as they slide over each other. These heterogeneous vibrations once started are propagated as elastic waves and are separated almost at once into two distinct wave types.[66] The one type of elastic wave consists of successive phases of condensation and rarefaction like sound in the air in which the particles vibrate in the direction of propagation of the wave. The other type of wave consists of distortions or twists, or shears, like the motion that was assumed in the old elastic theory of light,

121

in which the particles vibrate to and fro across the path of the wave. The first kind are often called longitudinal waves, or push-pull waves, or compression waves, or dilatation waves; the second kind are called transverse waves, or shear waves, or curl waves. The first kind of wave travels much faster and arrives first. Hence, in the Latin notation which has been adopted internationally, these waves are called *undae primae* and they are given the symbol P. Seismologists often speak of them simply as P-waves. The second kind of wave travels more slowly than the first so that it will arrive second. Hence these waves are called *undae secundae* and are given the symbol S. Thus they are often called S-waves. The ratio of the two velocities is roughly as nine is to five.

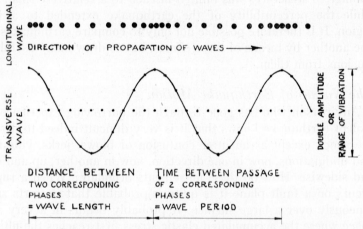

Fig. 120. Wave length and period in longitudinal and transverse waves.

It may be difficult for the casual reader to visualize these waves in the solid earth. They are not like water waves and they are totally different from the slow moving visible waves that are reported to have been seen traveling along the surface of the ground in some violent earthquakes. The waves of which we speak are elastic waves in which the motion of the solid ground is so slight that the eye cannot detect it and the speed is so great that the eye cannot follow. Their velocity is measured in thousands of feet per second or tens of thousands of miles per hour. It requires only about twenty minutes for waves of the first kind to reach the other side of the earth along a diameter. When body waves of these two types come to the surface of the earth they may and usually do generate other kinds of waves, elastic surface waves, which are also very rapid and invisible to the eye. These latter travel completely around the world in some three hours time.

Obviously, we cannot expect to measure such small and at the same time rapid motion except with delicate and sensitive instruments. In the field we can only infer the intensity of movement from the effects produced.

Meaning of Intensity

The word *intensity* has many meanings; but all of them are more or less significant of strength, violence, severity. In the physical sciences the word intensity is used quantitatively to denote relative strength, as, force per unit area, energy per unit volume. In the case of earthquakes we should likewise desire to have a quantitative measure of severity. But we are usually ignorant of the absolute value of the acceleration, or the force, or the energy. Therefore we are obliged to base our definition of intensity on such qualitative factors as *destructivity* and *perceptibility,* neither of which can be quantitatively correlated with any physical property of the motion.

Destructivity depends on the geological character of the ground on which the damaged structures were built, on their size and shape, on the character of the materials, on the design and workmanship. It obviously depends also on the force exerted by the wave, and therefore on the acceleration. It depends on the period of the wave because unison or resonance, which occurs when the period of the vibration and the natural period of the structure are the same, may play an important role by greatly increasing the range or amplitude of motion. It depends on velocity because the relative momentum in the differential vibrations of unit structures will govern in part the strength of their impact or the extent of their shear. It depends on time and therefore on the total energy, because a building may withstand the first shock and later yield to cumulative strains. But what relative part is played by each in determining the degree of intensity is quite unknown, although in a given set of circumstances the acceleration seems to be the decisive factor.

Perceptibility

On what factors does *sensibility* or *perceptibility* depend? An earthquake is felt more readily on the surface of the ground than it is in a mine; people in the upper stories of a tall building are more likely to feel the shock than those in the basement. One feels the waves more on loose ground than on firm rock. When the observer is at rest he is more likely to feel the oscillations than when he is walking or riding. But one person will feel an earthquake when another under the same conditions does not. The same person will perceive earthquakes much more readily after experiencing a severe shock than he did before. Obviously there is here a psychological element in addition to the purely physical factors. Yet the two questions that most interest the public and hence are most readily answered are precisely those used to measure intensity: (1) Where and how was the earthquake felt? and (2) What damage was done?

Scales of Intensity

The scales ordinarily used to indicate degrees of intensity of earthquake motion are of two types: *quantitative* and *qualitative*. The quantitative scales are mostly based on acceleration. The principal scales of this type that have been proposed are those of Omori,[67] Cancani,[68] McAdie,[69] Wood,[70] and Sieberg.[71] Holden[72] proposed a quantitative scale based on the kinetic energy of earthquake vibrations.

In so far as these various scales purport to assign an equivalence between absolute accelerations and degrees of perceptibility and destructivity, they are misleading and harmful. They give a semblance of precision that is totally lacking.

The two qualitative scales that have been most widely used in the past are the Rossi-Forel[73] and the second Mercalli[74] scales. A very useful summary of the history of modern scales of seismic intensity was published by Davison[75] in 1921.

Wood and Neumann[76] published a qualitative scale which is more useful in America than any of those previously employed. It is largely a development of Sieberg's[77] scale which in turn was based on Mercalli. We shall quote it in the abridged form.

ABRIDGED WOOD-NEUMANN SCALE

I. Not felt except by a very few under especially favorable circumstances.
II. Felt only by a few persons at rest, especially on upper floors of buildings. Delicately suspended objects may swing.
III. Felt quite noticeably indoors, especially on upper floors of build-

ings, but not recognized by many people as an earthquake. Standing motor cars may rock slightly. Vibration like passing of truck. Duration estimated.

IV. During the day felt indoors by many, outdoors by few. At night some awakened. Dishes, windows, doors disturbed; walls made cracking sound. Sensation like heavy truck striking building. Standing motor cars rocked noticeably.

V. Felt by nearly everyone; many awakened. Some dishes, windows, etc., broken; a few instances of cracked plaster; unstable objects overturned. Disturbance of trees, poles and other tall objects sometimes noticed. Pendulum clocks may stop.

VI. Felt by all; many frightened and run outdoors. Some heavy furniture moved; a few instances of fallen plaster or damaged chimneys. Damage slight.

VII. Everybody runs outdoors. Damage *negligible* in buildings of good design and construction; *slight* to moderate in well built ordinary structures; *considerable* in poorly built or badly designed structures; some chimneys broken. Noticed by persons driving motor cars.

VIII. Damage *slight* in specially designed structures; *considerable* in ordinary substantial buildings with partial collapse; *great* in poorly built structures. Panel walls thrown out of frame structures. Fall of chimneys, factory stacks, columns, monuments, walls. Heavy furniture overturned. Sand and mud ejected in small amounts. Changes in well water. Disturbed persons driving motor cars.

IX. Damage *considerable* in specially designed structures; well designed frame structures thrown out of plumb; *great* in substantial buildings, with partial collapse. Buildings shifted off foundations. Ground cracked conspicuously. Underground pipes broken.

X. Some well-built wooden structures destroyed; most masonry and frame structures destroyed with foundations; ground badly cracked. Rails bent. Landslides considerable from river banks and steep slopes. Shifted sand and mud. Water splashed (slopped) over banks.

XI. Few, if any (masonry), structures remain standing. Bridges destroyed. Broad fissures in ground. Underground pipelines completely out of service. Earth slumps and land slips in soft ground. Rails bent greatly.

XII. Damage total. Waves seen on ground surfaces. Lines of sight and level distorted. Objects thrown upward into the air.

Mapping of Seismic Intensity

If the region affected by an earthquake were geologically and physiographically homogeneous, densely populated throughout and occupied by a large number of more or less evenly spaced cities and towns of similar architecture, the mapping of relative intensities

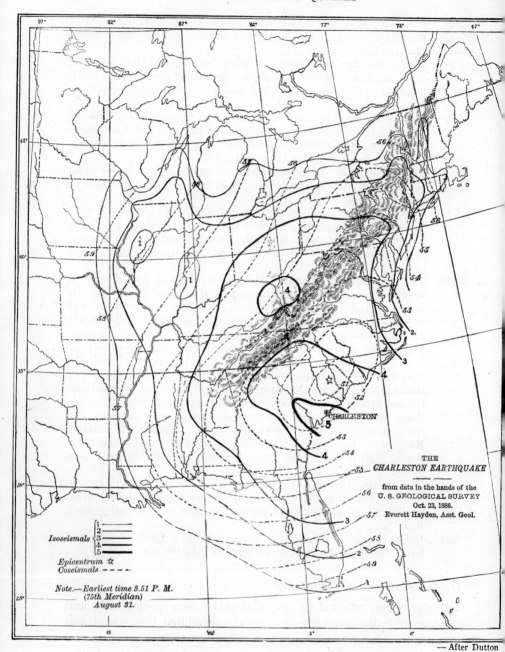

THE
CHARLESTON EARTHQUAKE

from data in the hands of the
U. S. GEOLOGICAL SURVEY
Oct. 23, 1886.
Everett Hayden, Asst. Geol.

Isoseismals
{1
2
3
4
5}

Epicentrum ☆
Coseismals - - - -.

Note.—Earliest time 3.51 P. M.
(75th Meridian)
August 31.

— After Dutton

Fig. 121. Isoseismal map of Charleston earthquake.

according to a suitable scale would be a comparatively simple task. But these conditions are seldom even approximately verified. The terrain may be partly mountainous, or forested, or desert. In one place the bed rock may be near the surface, in another deeply buried. Here the surface soil will be firm and dry; there it will be filled or reclaimed land or perhaps a marsh. One position will be a metropolitan area; another will be almost uninhabited. In one part the buildings may be of steel and concrete; in another of brick or stone; in still another of frame; in a fourth of mud or adobe. Under such circumstances it may be very difficult or quite impossible to construct a reliable map of intensities. Much of the territory in the western, southwestern, and northeastern United States, Canada, Mexico, and Central America, in great parts of South America, Asia, and Africa the conditions are so heterogeneous that precise mapping according to any detailed scale is often out of the question. Obviously such a map loses its meaning, or at least gives a false impression of accuracy, if its several parts are built on different criteria that are not strictly comparable.

Isoseismal Lines or Isoseists

An isoseist or isoseismal line is a curve drawn through all places on a map of seismic intensities at which the intensity has been found to be the same. Usually one such isoseismal line will be drawn for each of the grades or degrees in the chosen scale of intensity. Ideally each isoseismal line will be a smooth closed curve surrounding the one of next higher intensity. But practically these lines will be very irregular and there may be several smaller closed curves corresponding to one and the same intensity in isolated areas in addition to a principal one. Again it may be quite impossible to draw any objectively reliable isoseismal lines.

However, where the country is well populated so that large numbers of observations may be assembled from all parts of the area affected and where these can be investigated by an expert in the field, it is quite feasible to draw isoseismal lines or isoseists. Thus, for example, the isoseismal lines drawn by Dutton[78] for the Charleston earthquake of August 31, 1886, present a graphical summary of the data on the distribution of intensity. Maps containing isoseismals so constructed will be very useful in estimating the center of intensity of each shock, in ranking the shocks in order of violence, and in following the process of successive faulting.

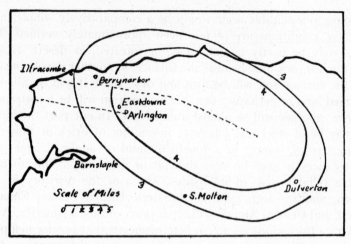

— After Davison

Fig. 122. Isoseismal map of the Exmoor earthquake.

In exceptionally favorable cases it may be possible so to evaluate geological and other differences as to reduce all observations to approximately the same basis in applying the arbitrary criteria of the scale of intensity. Conclusions may then be drawn with some confidence as to the strike and hade of the fault on which the slip has taken place. Thus Davison[79] was able to predict, by means of the isoseismal lines of the Exmoor, North Devonshire, earthquake of 1894, the presence and the strike and hade of a fault on the northern boundary of the Morte slates. The fault so mapped was found to be in close agreement with the field observations of Hicks,[80] though doubt was afterwards thrown[81] on some of the latter's conclusions.

The practical procedure in the construction of a map of seismic intensities on which isoseismal lines are to be drawn will be somewhat as follows:

(1) Immediately after the earthquake, while all impressions and observations are fresh in the minds of the people, several thousand simple questionnaires should be sent out so as to secure as large a number of answers as possible from every part of the area. The questionnaires must be so worded as to call for objective facts of observation and all their modifying circumstances without presenting a scale of intensity or asking for an estimate.

(2) An expert should be sent into the field to investigate every bit of information contained in the answers. Many statements will

be found to be erroneous, others exaggerated or inaccurate. A local psychology will often be found which has unconsciously influenced the answers. Thus, in some parts of the country any publicity about earthquakes is thought to be hurtful to business and there results a tendency not to report and to minimize or to attribute to other causes any earthquake phenomena that are forced on the attention. In other localities emulation evokes fanciful reports. The earthquake was felt in neighboring towns and local pride would be hurt if it could not boast as much. Even the trained investigator must be carefully on his guard against an all-too-human tendency to tell him what it is thought he would like to hear.

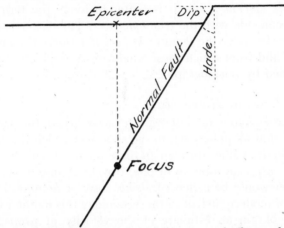

Fig. 123. Relation of the epicenter to the focus of an earthquake. Meaning of hade and dip of a fault.

(3) An expert should be directed to make an independent study of all damage that occurred at each place in the area, reassuring himself that it was really due to the particular earthquake under consideration and not to some other cause. He will note the character of the structures, whether they were well or poorly designed and built, and of what material they were constructed. He will study the geology of the region and determine the relation of the damaged and undamaged structures to it and to the physiography. He will estimate as nearly as possible the percentage of damaged to undamaged structures among those that were very poorly, ordinarily well, and very well built; among those located on marshy or reclaimed land, on deep alluvium or sand, and on rock.

(4) The expert must carefully weigh all the evidence and decide

while on the ground which of the twelve arbitrary degrees of the Wood-Neumann scale best describes the intensity of the earthquake at that place. The figure should be entered on a convenient map.

(5) If the entire map can be covered in this way by closely spaced scale numbers, it may be possible to draw a closed curve including all of the highest numbers and none that are lower; another curve enclosing all of the second highest numbers and none lower, and so on. These will be the desired *isoseismal lines*. They may have any shape because of irreducible inhomogeneities. But somewhere within the innermost curve it will be possible to designate the *center of intensity*. This point is often called the *macroseismic epicenter*, but it is better to avoid the term because it need not coincide with the true *epicenter*. This latter is the point perpendicularly above the *focus* or *hypocenter* where the fault movement *starts* and from which those waves proceed which are the first to be recorded by seismographs.

Coseismal Lines or Homoseists

If it were possible to determine exactly when the earthquake waves arrived at all points within the area over which the shock was felt, we could draw lines through all those points at which the motion arrived, say, after an interval of one, two, three minutes and so on. These curves would be called *coseismal lines* or *homoseists*. Before the advent of modern instrumental seismology this method was often followed to obtain an estimate of the velocity of propagation of earthquake waves. Thus coseismal lines were drawn by Dutton on the map of the Charleston earthquake. However, the methods used were so crude and timekeeping everywhere left so much to be desired that the errors in estimating the time of arrival of the waves were often of the same order of magnitude as the total time of travel of the waves, for the speed of travel of longitudinal waves in the deeper parts of the earth's crust and in the subcrustal materials varies from about 5.5 kilometers per second (3.4 miles per sec.) to as high as 13.5 kilometers per second (8.4 miles per sec.). Coming up to the curved surface of the earth at an angle, these waves *appear* to travel along the surface at a much higher speed. Thus we see how hopeless it really is to attempt to time the arrivals by looking at one's watch or observing the time of stoppage of clocks, even if these were keeping perfectly correct time. We must, therefore, take these older coseismal maps with many grains of salt.

Chapter VII

SEA QUAKES AND SEISMIC SEA WAVES

About three fourths of the earth's surface is under water. Earthquakes also occur in these submerged portions of the crust. The exact location of these earthquakes is quite as important for the study of seismic geography and of the earth's internal structure as is that of earthquakes whose origin is on land. That they are very numerous and are similar in every respect to earthquakes originating on land is known from the records of land-based seismographs. But is it possible to study them without instruments? The field methods of the previous chapter are clearly inapplicable to submarine earthquakes.

When an earthquake is felt on land it is called a *land quake* or simply earthquake. When it is felt at sea it is called a *sea quake*. A *sea quake* then is the quaking sensation felt by those aboard vessels that happen to be in the neighborhood when the earthquake occurs. The sensation caused by the shock is as though the vessel were striking and pounding on a submerged reef. The pulses coming up from below through the water strike the ship almost vertically. The water is actually hammering on the ship's bottom. Why? The reason is this: Earthquake waves travel in all directions from their source in the crust of the earth where the rock slip has occurred. Some of them thus impinge on the boundary between the rock and water at the bottom of the ocean. But these cannot continue into the water just as they are. In the first place no transverse waves can pass through a fluid like water or air. And in the second place the longitudinal waves are greatly slowed up by the water. So what happens? Most of the wave energy is reflected back down into the earth and what little does get through comes almost straight up as longitudinal wave pulses.

Sea quakes are usually reported by the officers of vessels which experience them and, in the case of American ships, the longitude

131

and latitude of the vessel at the time the shock was felt are printed
on the backs of charts issued by the United States Hydrographic
Office. These printed reports are very helpful to seismologists in the
location of the earthquake.

Seismic Sea Waves

A relatively small number of violent submarine earthquakes have
a dreaded sequel, a flood wave, which is popularly known as a *tidal
wave* in English-speaking countries, and in French-speaking lands as
a *raz de marée*, although it has nothing to do with ordinary tides. In
Japan it is called *tunami*, or *tsunami*.

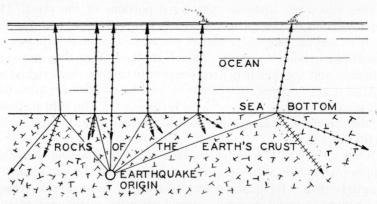

Fig. 124. Waves from a sea quake bent by refraction at the ocean
bottom so that they strike ships almost vertically. Note that most
of the energy is reflected back into the earth both as longitudinal
waves and transverse waves, only a fraction entering the water,
and this only in the form of longitudinal waves.

The mechanism of these waves is somewhat obscure. However,
when an earthquake involves a permanent vertical displacement of
the ocean floor, either on the two sides of a submarine fault or by
reason of the uplift or depression of an adjacent continental shelf or
island mass, the hydrostatic equilibrium is thereby disturbed. We
should expect the water to flow away from the portion of the sea
bed that is relatively raised and toward the part that is relatively
lowered. Once the flow is started the momentum acquired by the
water will carry it too far and it will pile up over the lowered area
until the accumulated head reverses the flow, thus initiating a series
of oscillations in the disturbed area and a corresponding train of
translation waves concentrically around it. As these waves diverge

Fig. 125. "Tidal wave" or tunami breaking on a beach.

outward in all directions from their source they rapidly diminish in height and increase in length until they approximate the character of tides and are scarcely perceptible on the high seas.

As these waves approach the land, however, the picture changes. Many things can happen. On a sloping shore the sea may be observed to withdraw only to return in a long unbroken wall. The bottom of this first wave is retarded by friction and the top is pushed forward so much faster than the bottom that the wave is tripped and comes rolling in like a breaker. The height of the seismic sea wave on reaching the shore does not depend only on the mass of water displaced at the origin and on the height of the wave on the open sea, but is modified by the slope of the sea bed and by the curvature of the shore line. The height of the sea waves which caused a part of the damage and considerable loss of life in the Messina earthquake of December 28, 1908, varied from place to place along the Sicilian and Calabrian coasts. At Messina the height was only seven feet while farther south on the opposite shore it reached a maximum of thirty feet. The seismic sea wave which followed the Hawaiian earthquake of 1868 is said to have rolled in over the tops of cocoanut trees. After the Sanriku earthquake of June 15, 1896, which occurred on the Tuscarora Deep off the northeastern coast of the main island of Japan, the water in Miyako Bay began to recede about 7:50 p.m., eighteen minutes after the earthquake was felt in Miyako. About eight o'clock the crest of the first wave swept

over the city. This wave was followed by another which is said to
have reached the height of ninety-three feet. Five more waves followed before the energy of the disturbance was spent. On March 3,
1933, another violent submarine earthquake occurred at almost the
same spot on the western slope of the Tuscarora Deep about 150
miles off shore; and again Miyako and the coast of the Iwate prefecture were swept by distastrous tunami. Where the shore was
precipitous there was merely a rise and a fall of water. Where the
sea bed sloped the wave came in shore as a wall of water sweeping
away everything movable. Even a massive concrete sea wall was
broken and tossed about. At inlets the onrushing waters created
powerful currents carrying away whole villages and rolling inland
like the bore of a tide. When the ebb set in, some of the wreckage
was left stranded but much was carried far out to sea.

Such waves may even carry away large vessels, breaking their
anchor chains, and perhaps leaving them stranded far inland, as
they did the *U.S.S. Wateree* after the Chilean earthquake of August
13, 1868.

On entering a gulf or bay seismic sea waves may initiate what
are known as seiches. A *seiche* is a to and fro vibration of a body
of water in its own natural tempo like the slopping of water in a
jolted basin. Once started, the water body will continue to oscillate
independently with its own proper period. Seismic sea waves are
only one of the many causes of seiches which often occur also in
lakes and ponds.

Once a seismic sea wave is started on its way by an earthquake,
its course and its velocity are independent of the source. The seismic
sea waves generated by the Iquique earthquake of 1877 traveled
from the coast of South America entirely across the Pacific Ocean
to Japan and were recorded with an amplitude of about eight feet
by the tide gauges at Hakodate, 10,300 miles distant from their
source. Their velocity depends on the depth of the water which
varies in different parts of the oceans. Davison[82] gives the following
observed values for the Pacific Ocean.

Earthquake	Distance in km.	Time h.	m.	Velocity km./hr.	mi./hr.
Japan, 1854	9,000	12	37	714	443
Japan, 1896	7,700	10	34	730	453
Iquique, 1868	16,600	24	57	665	413
Valparaiso, 1906	17,600	23	31	749	465

Therefore, an approximate value for the speed across the Pacific would be 450 miles per hour. In the shallower Atlantic Ocean the speed is much less. In the case of the Grand Banks earthquake of 1929 it was apparently only about 200 miles per hour.

Chapter VIII

EARTHQUAKES IN THE AIR

Perhaps the most mysterious and intriguing of all earthquake phenomena are the sounds that come out of the earth.[83] Noises that are heard in destructive earthquakes are of two kinds. First, there are sounds that do not come from the ground, such as the creaking and groaning of buildings; the crashing of masonry, bricks, plaster, dishes, glassware, crockery, and furniture; the barking and howling of dogs, the frightened cries of birds, and other animals. Second, there are earthquake noises properly so called which actually emanate from the ground and are transmitted into the air in the same manner as the longitudinal vibrations in sea quakes. Both air and water are fluids of low viscosity and consequently are incapable of transmitting the transverse vibrations of earthquakes.

However, there is an important difference between sea quake vibrations and earthquake sounds that makes for the greater mysteriousness of the latter. It is this: the vibrations which come up through the water from the bottom of the sea and are transmitted to the hull of a ship may be felt through a wide range of frequencies. But it is the sense of *feeling* through which the shock is perceived by those on board the vessel. Earthquake sounds are *heard*, not felt. It is the ear through which they are perceived, and the human ear is only sensitive to a very limited range of frequencies. Besides, the upper and lower limits of hearing are not the same for every person. The lower threshold varies between sixteen and thirty vibrations per second. On the other hand, an unbelievably small amount of energy in sound waves will suffice to make them audible if their pitch is right.

Now we know from instrumental records of earthquakes that most of the waves in the ground have frequencies below the human threshold of hearing and that the spectrum of frequencies varies from one shock to another.

All these facts go far toward explaining why earthquake *sounds* are connected with one shock and not with another; why they are heard in one part of the area in which an earthquake is felt and not in another part; why the distribution of loudness does not correspond with that of intensity of earthquake motion as measured by degrees of destructivity and perceptibility of the ground vibration; why, when two persons are standing side by side, the one sometimes hears nothing while the other hears a deafening roar; and finally, why the sound may be heard before the earthquake vibration is actually felt, or may not be heard until the felt shock has passed, or may even be heard when no earthquake is otherwise noticed.

If no sound was heard by anyone at the time of the earthquake, it probably means that audible frequencies were absent in the ground motion, as often happens. If sounds are heard in some places and not in other parts of the area where the earthquake was distinctly felt, this condition may be due either to differences in the surface rocks of the earth which damped out the higher frequencies in some places more than in others or it may be due to an asymmetrical radiation of the shorter waves at the origin of the earthquake, or to the variation of the angle at which the waves in the solid earth struck the boundary between earth and air because this angle of incidence has considerable influence on the amount of wave energy that will be refracted into the air as audible sound.

It is less easy to understand why sound which travels so slowly — only about one-fifth of a mile per second in air — can be heard before the waves are felt in the ground although these travel so very much faster — the true speed reaching up to four miles a second and the apparent velocity very much higher if the earthquake originated at any appreciable depth. Obviously sounds cannot outrun the ground vibrations. A plausible explanation that is sometimes advanced is this: Suppose that the very first motion of the ground in a particular earthquake is very slight but rapid and is followed only later by a strong shock. The first waves in the ground might not be noticed because there was not enough energy in them. On the other hand the conditions might be just right for the refraction into the air of a large percentage of this modicum of energy, so that the noise might seem loud; for it is surprising what little energy is actually present in sounds that appear loud to the human ear.

Another very plausible explanation for the hearing of earthquake noises before the shock is felt is based on the separation of the longi-

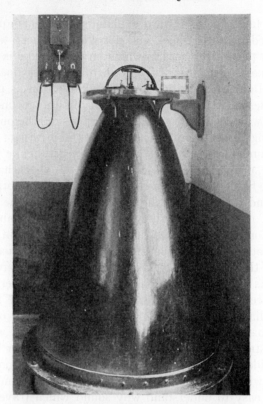

— Photo by Rev. B. F. Doucette, S.J.

Fig. 126. "Geophone" designed by a Manila Jesuit, built in Paris, and installed at the Manila Observatory in 1886. Sounds produced in a cylindrical hole in the ground were focused on a microphone (with a wooden diaphragm) by the copper paraboloid above the hole and were heard in the earphones. The microphone also actuated a bell to call the observer.

tudinal and transverse waves in the ground motion. The longitudinal waves not only travel almost twice as fast as transverse waves but they also contain vibrations of much higher frequency which would contribute to audible sound. This explanation could only apply if the interval between the sound and the felt shock is the same as that between the arrivals of longitudinal and transverse waves and the longitudinal waves were relatively weak.

In those cases in which the noises are heard after the shock is over, it is probable that no audible sound was generated locally by the passage of the earthquake waves and that the sound comes from some distant locality where conditions were favorable. It is a fact of observation that the sounds which are heard are usually of low frequency, very near the lower threshold of hearing. Oftentimes they are described as a deep booming, or a rumble, or a low moan.

Finally we have those extremely interesting cases in which the characteristic noises are heard but no shock is felt at all. There are places where sounds are heard so frequently as to receive a name such as *Barisal guns, mist poeffers, Moodus noises*. Are these earthquakes? Only instrumental investigations can decide.

Scales of Earthquake Sounds

A scale of sound intensity is obviously necessary for the field study of earthquakes that are heard but not felt and furnishes useful information in other earthquakes also. Empirical scales of sound intensity were devised by Knott and by Davison. The following is a slight abbreviation of the scale used by Davison[84] in the study of British earthquakes.

1. Trains passing over a bridge or through a tunnel; dragging of heavy boxes or furniture over the floor.
2. Thunder, a loud clap or heavy peal, but most often distant thunder.
3. Wind moaning, roaring or rough and strong; the howling of wind in a gap or chimney; a chimney on fire.
4. Loads of stones falling, as when tipped.
5. Fall of heavy bodies, the banging of a door, the blow of a wave on the sea shore.
6. Explosions, distant blasting, the boom of a distant heavy gun.
7. Miscellaneous, such as the trampling of many animals, an immense covey of partridges on the wing, the roar of a waterfall, a low pedal note on an organ, and the rending or settling together of huge masses of rock.

Thus the sound is a jumble of noises whose pitch or frequency is very near the lower limit of audibility. And since this threshold varies, as we have said, from person to person, only a certain percentage of the population ordinarily will hear it. If enough data are available this percentage may be determined for all parts of the area affected.

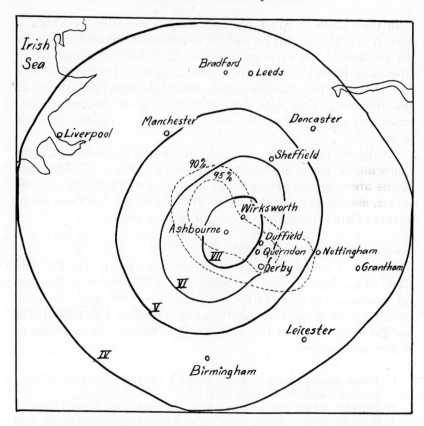

— After Davison

Fig. 127. Isacoustic lines (dotted) and their relation to the iso-seismal lines (full) of the Derby earthquake of March 24, 1903.

Isacoustic Lines

Davison's method of studying the sound pattern of an earthquake was to determine what he called isacoustic lines. "An isacoustic line," according to Davison, "is a line drawn through all places at which the same percentage of the total number of observers in it are capable of hearing the earthquake sound," or more tersely, "Isacoustic lines are lines which pass through all points at which the percentage of audibility is the same." In general, both isoseismal and isacoustic lines enclose the same general region of origin of the earthquake. But the two sets of curves do not always indicate precisely the same point as source. The isacoustic lines are frequently eccentric with respect to the system of isoseismal lines.

Chapter IX

STUDY OF EARTHQUAKES WITH INSTRUMENTS

The Problem

In the region of maximum intensity of a destructive earthquake the movement of the ground can be felt; but the movement is so complicated in itself and at the same time so disconcerting to the observer and so productive of psychological reactions that it is practically impossible to obtain a correct and reliable record by direct personal observation. At greater distances from the epicenter the vibration is more regular, but soon becomes imperceptible to the unaided senses. Therefore, throughout the entire range of distances it is necessary to use some type of recording instrument in order to determine the motion of the ground. Such an instrument is called *seismoscope* if it merely indicates the presence of earthquake motion, a *seismometer* if it measures how much the earth is moving, and a *seismograph* (pronounced size'-mo-graf) if it makes a permanent record of the motion.

The Seismograph

The object of a seismograph is to record as accurately as possible at each successive instant of time the direction, magnitude, and other characteristics of the ground motion, or to record something from which the correct motion and the force that produced it can be easily deduced. It is clear that the absolute motion as such cannot be observed directly. When we observe a moving body, such as a falling object, a racing automobile, or a train in motion, we use the ground and the surroundings, or the floor and walls of a building as a frame of reference in relation to which the motion is determined; but in an earthquake the whole building and all the surroundings, including the ground, are in motion, so that there is no stationary frame of reference.

The Ideal

If we could step from the earth to a nearby planetoid and observe from that independent vantage point the movement of the ground and of all objects attached to it, there would be no difficulty in determining the magnitude and direction of the motion relatively to ourselves; but it is obviously impossible either to secure such a planetoid, or to keep it independent of forces exerted by the earth if we had it and could make observation on it.

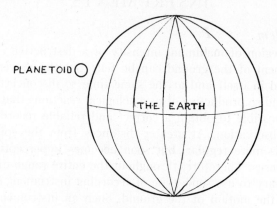

Fig. 128. Free planetoid, an ideal earthquake displacement meter.

Substitute

The best we can do is to make the attachment or coupling between a body with inertia and the earth as loose as possible. The less rigid the connection the more will the relative motion between the body and the ground represent the motion of the ground relative to the earth as a whole. As viewed from the ground the apparent motion of the body will approximate the exact reverse of the motion of the ground as viewed from the body. However, there is a practical limit to the looseness of the bond or connection. Any connection whatever will disturb the relative motion; hence it will be necessary to correct the observed relative motion by taking away that part of it which is due to the connection between the body and the earth. This correction is in general very difficult, but there are some simple cases in which it can be done with some precision.

Components of Earthquake Motion

The most general displacement of the ground relative to the earth as a whole may be resolved into six independent components: three translations parallel to three mutually perpendicular directions or axes, and three rotations around these axes. If we are not too near the origin of the earthquake, the rotations will be so small that they can be safely neglected, as has been shown by repeated experiments. There remain, then, the three translations, the directions of which we may choose as north, east, and vertical.

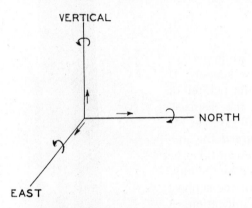

Fig. 129. Six components of earth-quake motion.

Fig. 130. Weighted spring acted on by the force of gravity.

Measurement of Vertical Motion

Let us take the measurement of the vertical motion as our first problem. Let us suppose a metal weight suspended by a helical spring from a fixed support. The force of gravity acting on the suspended mass of metal will pull it downward and elongate the spring until the elastic force thus brought into play will exactly counterbalance the downward pull of gravity acting on the mass. Thus, in a condition of equilibrium there are two balanced forces, the downward pull of gravity and the upward pull of the spring. Let us suppose, for simplicity, that the weight of the spring is negligible in comparison with that of the suspended mass and that the mass is prevented from moving horizontally by frictionless guides between which it slides. In a state of equilibrium there is a definite distance between the center of the mass and the support. This we can measure. If we displace the mass upward or downward so that it is no longer in equilibrium and then release it, it will vibrate up and down. We can observe the relative distance at any instant between the mass and the support. But if we have no other frame of reference it will be impossible for us to deduce whether the mass is moving upward or the support downward. If we fix our attention on the suspended mass as though it were standing still, the support will seem to be vibrating. If we attach an indicator to the suspended mass and set up behind it a scale fastened to the support we shall be able to measure the relative motion between them.

Magnification

Now let us suppose that we impart an up-and-down motion to the support. If the distance traveled by the pointer or indicator is greater than the displacement of the support we shall say that the weighted spring has *magnified* the motion of the support; and we can take the ratio of the distance traveled by the indicator to the displacement of the support as a measure of this magnification. A given force exerted by the vibrating support will produce in a stiff spring a smaller relative motion between it and the indicator than the same force will produce in a weak spring, because it will require a smaller elongation of a stiff spring to bring into play a given elastic force than will be acquired of a weak spring. We should therefore say that a mass suspended on a stiff spring is less sensitive to displacement of the support than the same mass supported on a weak spring. The tendency of the mass to move would seem to be greater for the weak spring than for the strong spring. Thus there would be an inherent tendency for the weight on a weak spring to

— Photo by Rev. B. F. Doucette, S.J.

Fig. 131. Spiral spring pendulum whose bob pushes down an indicator on the scale below. Installed at the Manila Observatory for the measurement of vertical motion prior to 1869.

magnify motions of the support more than the same weight on a stiff spring. This effect of the restoring force is a property inherent in the system under all circumstances.

Lever Magnification

Taking a step farther we could attach a writing point to the suspended mass by means of a lever with the fulcrum nearer to the mass. The trace or mark made by the writing point would then be greater than the relative movement between the mass and the support in proportion to the lengths of the two lever arms. The ratio between the length of the trace and the displacement of the support will be the true magnification or dynamic magnification, whereas the ratio between the length of the trace and the displacement of the mass will be the static magnification. The latter is dependent only on the construction of the system.

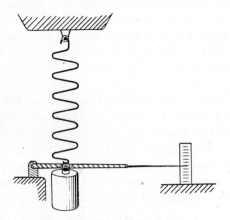

Fig. 132. Magnifying lever.

Free Period and Dynamic Magnification

The dynamic magnification is also dependent on the relative speed with which the support is moved, or on the period of its vibrations. There are three possible kinds of motion of the weight resulting from a displacement of the support. In the first kind in which the support is raised and lowered very rapidly the mass will remain stationary because of its inertia and of the loose coupling. In this

kind of motion we have a situation resembling that of a free planetoid. In the second kind where there is a very slow upward or downward movement of the support, the mass will move along with the
support and the relative distance between the mass and the support
will remain unchanged; that is, there will be close or tight coupling
and no relative motion. As a first step toward an understanding of
the third kind of motion, let us suppose the support to remain stationary and the mass to be pulled downward a short distance and
then released. The force of gravity pulling on the mass will be practically the same as before, whereas the pull of the spring will be
greater, because the elastic force is proportional to the elongation
of the spring. Therefore, since there is an unbalanced force pulling
upward on the mass, the latter will move upward and in doing so
will acquire momentum which will carry it beyond the position of
equilibrium at which the upward and downward forces are equal.
Thus the mass moving upward will become subject to an unbalanced
downward force which will eventually stop it and start it moving
downward. Thus will be generated a series of oscillations, each of
which will be executed in a given interval of time, which is called
the *period* of the vibration. For a given weight supported by a
given spring the period is a fixed quantity, or the free period of the
system.

Now let us suppose the mass to be at rest and let us return to the
motions of the support. If the up-and-down movement of the latter
is neither very rapid nor very slow we shall have a condition in
which the mass will acquire a motion of its own, the *amplitude* or
greatest displacement of which will depend not merely on the magnitude of the unbalanced force exerted by the vibrating support but
on the tempo of its repeated applications.

Resonance

The effect will be greatest when the support is vibrated up and
down in step with the mass, that is, when the support has the same
period of vibration as the weighted spring. Under these circumstances each downward movement of the mass will be accompanied
by the application of a downward force which will tend to speed it
up and increase the range of downward movement and each upward
motion of the mass will be accompanied by an unbalanced upward
pull which will further increase its range of movement. This condition of synchronism or equality of periods is known as the state of

resonance and there is theoretically no limit to the amplitude or range of vibration which may be acquired by the suspended mass under these circumstances. Therefore, the third kind of motion induced by the vibration of the support is one in which there is partial or complete resonance. It is clear that in the third kind of motion in contrast with the second kind — in which we are unable to measure the displacement of the support at all since there is no relative motion between it and the weight — we may deduce the motion by proper dynamic analysis. However, we are not able to measure the displacement directly, since the relative motion between the support and the mass is masked by the large proper motions of the weighted spring itself.

Magnification Ratio

Applying this reasoning to our loosely coupled planetoid we see that in the first case the apparent displacement of the planetoid as viewed from the ground is an exact measure of the magnitude of the actual displacement of the ground; that is, the relative displacement of the planetoid is in a ratio of 1 to 1 to that of the ground. The ratio, therefore, between the dynamic magnification and the static magnification will be 1 to 1. In the second case in which there is no relative motion, so that the planetoid follows the ground, the ratio of the relative motion of the tightly coupled planetoid to the actual displacement of the ground is 0 to 1, and therefore the ratio of the dynamic magnification to the static magnification is 0. In the third case the ratio of the apparent motion of the planetoid to the actual displacement of the ground increases as we approach the state of resonance or equalization of periods, when the ratio of the dynamic magnification to the static magnification becomes theoretically infinite. Thus, if we plot points on a diagram with the ratio of the period of the ground to the natural period of the loosely coupled planetoid as abscissae and the corresponding ratio of the dynamic magnification to the static magnification as ordinates, and if we draw a curve through all of these points, this magnification curve will rise from a value of 1 when the period ratio is very small — that is, when the vibration of the ground is relatively very rapid — to a theoretically infinite value when the two periods are equal and will then drop off to 0 as the period of the ground becomes very much greater than the natural period of the coupled planetoid.

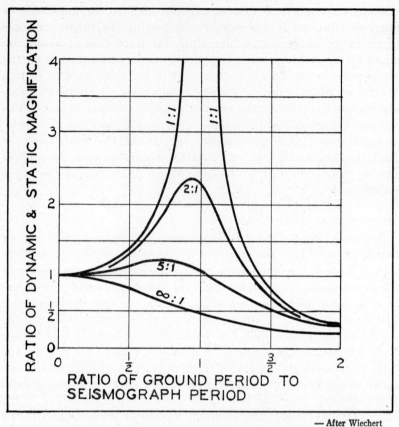

— After Wiechert

Fig. 133. Curves showing the effect of damping proportional to velocity on the ratio of dynamic to static magnification as wave period changes in relation to the free period of the pendulum.

Damping

It is possible to equalize this response to a certain extent by introducing into the coupling a force which will oppose the relative motion of the planetoid with respect to the ground. If this resisting force is solid friction we may move the ground within certain limits without producing any corresponding relative motion of the plane-toid. Its motion is prevented by solid friction until the unbalanced force acting on the planetoid becomes greater than the frictional force which tends to hold the planetoid stationary. We therefore lose the advantage of the loose coupling and the planetoid becomes effectively a part of the ground within those limits. A type of resisting force that will avoid this difficulty is one which is proportional to the speed of the relative motion between the planetoid and the ground. Such a force would be, for example, the resistance produced by a short circuited coil of copper wire moving in a magnetic field. When the ground starts to move, the planetoid experiences no resistance at first; but the faster the relative motion of the planetoid

— Photo by Rev. B. F. Doucette, S.J.

Fig. 134. A simple pendulum seismograph constructed in Paris for the Manila Observatory about 1888. A loose pin in the bottom of the bob writes on a smoked spherical plate.

becomes, the more it is held back. The effect of such force is to decrease the dynamic magnification in the region of resonance and to flatten out the magnification ratio curve. When the damping force is increased to such a degree that the planetoid when deflected from its position of equilibrium returns exactly to it without crossing over to the other side, the damping is said to be critical.

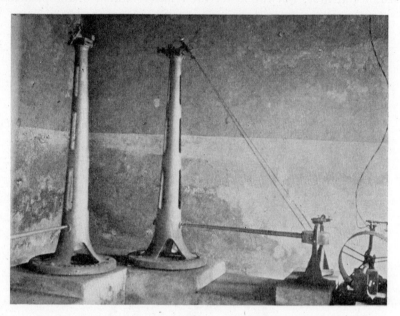

Fig. 135. Small horizontal pendulum formerly operated by the United States Coast and Geodetic Survey at its geomagnetic observatory in Cheltenham, Maryland.

Measurement of Horizontal Motion

In order to measure a translation toward the east or north, it will be necessary to set up another independent type of loose coupled planetoid which will respond only to horizontal movement of the ground. An ordinary pendulum approximates this type of response for small amplitudes of motion, but the coupling is rather tight and the restoring force is so large for any given displacement of the pendulum that the intrinsic sensitivity is very small. The coupling may be loosened by turning the axis of rotation of the pendulum nearly into a vertical position so that only a very small component of the force of gravity is effective as a restoring force. This type of instrument is called a horizontal pendulum. We can distinguish as before the three kinds of movement: first, when the movement of the ground is very rapid, second, when it is very slow in proportion to the period of the pendulum, and third, when the period of vibratory motion of the ground approaches that of the pendulum. The dynamics in each case are the same as for the spring pendulum.

Displacement Meters

Now, if the earthquake vibrations were all of the same frequency we could choose the period of the recording system or seismograph so much greater than that of the earthquake vibrations that we should always be dealing with the first case. Then the motion of the ground would be obtained by reversing the relative motion of the recording system and dividing its magnitude by the static magnification. But earthquake waves are not so obliging. It has been said that the vibrations in near earthquakes are of short period, whereas those in distant earthquakes are of long period. This is a misleading statement. It is true that certain types of earthquake waves tend to lengthen as they travel, also that short waves are damped out more rapidly than long waves, but these are minor factors. Each earthquake sets up vibrations with a wide range of frequencies. In general, the stronger and more violent the earthquake the more waves of long period it will radiate, but on these longer waves there will be superposed a great number of shorter ones. If we were to resolve the wave motion of a strong earthquake into all its component frequencies we should find a whole spectrum of periods ranging from a small fraction of a second to many minutes in length. It is practically impossible to construct a seismograph whose period will be very much longer than all these periods. And with any intermediate value of the seismograph period the phenomenon of resonance will come into play. The waves whose period is near that of the pendulum will be exaggerated at the expense of all the others. A pure displacement meter for earthquakes is therefore impossible.

Accelerographs

A second choice presents itself. We may try to make the free period of the pendulum or other device so short that the ratio of the wave period to the free period of the recording system will always be much greater than one to one and thus avoid resonance.

This is a useful choice for many purposes because the response of such a system is in step with the force or acceleration instead of with the ground motion. However, it does not solve our problem for the recording of earthquakes because, as we have seen, the dynamic magnification drops off to zero for waves that are much longer than the free period of the recording system. Hence, the shorter waves are exaggerated at the expense of longer ones and the very long waves are sacrificed altogether.

Recording Speed

There is still a further difficulty in the construction of our seismographs. There must be a certain relation between the wave length and the amplitude of a wave as recorded, to permit us readily to recognize the wave form. If the time scale of the record is so compressed that long waves are readily identified the rapid vibrations will follow so close upon one another that they will be superposed and lost on the record. If, on the other hand, the time scale is so open that very rapid vibrations are clearly resolved, the long waves will be so flat that they will probably escape our notice.

No Unique Solution

It is clear, then, that satisfactory observation of earthquake motion in strong and weak shocks, in near earthquakes and distant earthquakes will require seismographs of several different types. In fact each seismograph must be designed specially for the work it is to do. We shall discuss seismographs for engineering and for seismic prospecting, and seismographs for the continual vibrations we call microseisms, in later chapters. But even for natural earthquakes seismographs of many different types are needed. Each will bring to our attention features of the earthquake that were not at all apparent from the records of the others. The ideal would be a scale of three-component seismographs ranging from short-period, open-scale seismographs to long-period, compressed-scale instruments, which would respond to the different frequencies of oncoming earthquake waves like a series of organ pipes or piano strings. Nor would this alone suffice. A third factor that must be considered in the construction of seismographs is the range of motion that must be observed or the force that must be measured. The force exerted near the origin of a violent earthquake may approach, or even surpass, in magnitude the force of gravity; whereas at a great distance from the origin the force to be observed may be as small as one one-hundred-millionth part of the force of gravity. A seismograph designed for the latter would be useless in recording the former, and vica versa, yet earthquakes may occur at any distance from the recording station, and if a station is to record all of them it must be equipped with instruments having a large range of magnification from very high to very low.

Chapter X

SEISMOGRAPHS FOR NATURAL EARTHQUAKES

It is clear from the preceding chapter that the designing of the instrumental equipment for a seismographic station is no simple matter. Let us trace briefly the development of seismographs in response to all these conflicting demands. Up to the last quarter of the nineteenth century the instruments devised for the observation of earthquakes were for the most part not seismographs but seismoscopes, such as the interesting device constructed by a Chinaman, Chang Heng, nearly two thousand years ago. With the coming of the little group of Englishmen to man the newly established Japanese universities in the early seventies of the last century a new era of instrumental construction began. Spurred on by John Milne, a mining engineer whose attention was at once attracted to the many earthquakes which occurred in Japan, the physicists Ewing, Gray, Perry, and Knott designed pendulums to record the three perpendicular components of translation in earthquake waves. They or-

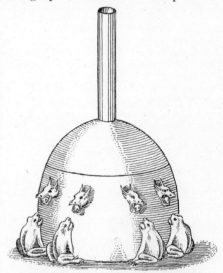

— After drawing by John Milne

Fig. 136. Seismoscope constructed in China by Chang Heng (called in Japan, Tyoko, or Choko, or Cho-i-Cho) about the beginning of the Christian Era. Inside of this instrument a pillar is suspended which sways at the time of an earthquake, at the same time making a record of it. The swaying pillar knocks the ball out of that dragon's mouth, on the outside of the instrument, which is in the direction of the swaying pillar. The frog underneath that particular dragon receives the ball and vibrates vigorously, thus giving the direction of an earthquake.

— Photo by Rev. B. F. Doucette, S.J.

Fig. 137. Gray-Milne three-component seismograph installed at the Manila Observatory in 1888. The two horizontal and one vertical spring pendulums were each connected by levers to pens writing on a paper strip which ordinarily moved slowly but was speeded up whenever an earthquake shook the brass ball at the bottom to a new position.

— Photo by Rev. B. F. Doucette, S.J.

Fig. 138. Cecchi seismograph (Cf. Gerlands Beiträge zur Geophysik, Vol. 3, pp. 436–437) installed at the Manila Observatory in 1882. Records horizontal and vertical movements.

ganized a Seismological Society of Japan and one of their pupils, Fusakichi Omori, became the leader of Japanese seismologists, but these instruments were all intended for the observation of local earthquakes occurring in Japan. In the meantime the German scientist, Von Rebeur-Paschwitz, found that his delicate pendulums designed for the measurement of the tidal effects of the sun and moon were disturbed by earthquakes on the other side of the earth. The news spread throughout the scientific world and instruments began to be constructed for the observation of distant earthquakes in Japan,

Fig. 139. The Milne-Shaw seismograph with covers removed.

Italy, and Germany. With the return of the group of English scientists from Japan to England, Milne took up his residence at Shide on the Isle of Wight and there developed a type of horizontal pendulum with photographic registration which he tried to spread through the world, but his instruments gave records of comparatively low magnification and especially with such a compressed time scale that their usefulness was limited. J. J. Shaw, after Milne's death, redesigned the seismograph and the Milne-Shaw pendulums are now in use in a large number of stations. Wiechert in Germany was impressed by the Italian method of recording on smoked paper and devised a type of inverted pendulum whose movements were magnified by means of a series of levers in which the friction was reduced to a minimum by substitution of flat springs for hinges. Of the smaller type of the instrument a large number were imported into this country and installed in Jesuit colleges and universities between 1909 and 1911, largely on the initiative of the late Reverend Frederick L. Odenbach, S.J., of John Carroll University in Cleveland, and have been in use for a quarter of a century. Wiechert also built similar seismographs for the registration of the vertical component. Two types of horizontal pendulums that have been in wide use during past decades are the Bosch-Omori and the Mainka. McComb has improved the Bosch-Omori type by introducing Romberg's tilt-compensation. However, a new era of seismographic construction was ushered in by Galitzin when about 1910 he introduced the principle of electromagnetic induction and galvanometric recording in his vertical and horizontal seismographs. After the first World War the Cambridge Instrument Company in England built vertical and horizontal seismographs of the Galitzin type. Wilip designed a much more compact and serviceable form of the Galitzin

— Photo by Rev. B. F. Doucette, S.J.

Fig. 140. Wiechert 955 kilogram inverted pendulum horizontal component seismograph installed at the Manila Observatory in 1910.

Fig. 141. Side view of small Wiechert horizontal component
seismograph.

Fig. 142.   Detail of small Wiechert horizontal component seismograph.

Fig. 143. Small Wiechert vertical-component seismograph.

electromagnetic seismograph. One of the faults of the vertical-
component seismograph of Galitzin, Wiechert, and others was the
dependence of the period on the displacement of the pendulum. This
was corrected in great measure by Wilip who distributed the mass
of the pendulum and the elastic action of the springs in such a
manner about the hinge that the restoring force retained the same
proportion to the displacement on both sides of the position of
equilibrium. Wenner designed an electromagnetic seismograph that
was more compact than either that of Galitzin or Wilip and which
had a much flatter magnification curve and a better response to
short-period earth movements than either of the others. In order to
obtain high magnifications with mechanical recording on smoked
paper De Quervain and Piccard constructed a universal seismograph
for all three components whose moving mass was twenty tons. A
number of these are now in use in Europe. In contrast to this
enormous mass, Wood and Anderson designed the torsion seismometer whose mass consists of a very small copper cylinder attached to the side of a filament of tungsten one-fiftieth of a millimeter in diameter and a few inches in length. When the ground is
displaced, the inertia of the copper cylinder causes it to rotate about

the filament and a beam of light reflected from a mirror attached
to the cylinder traces a wavy line on photographic paper carried by
a rotating drum. Benioff has designed a seismometer which in itself

— Courtesy U. S. Coast and Geodetic Survey

Fig. 144. McComb-Romberg tilt compensation
seismometer. Horizontal pendulums when operating at periods in excess of ten seconds are
very sensitive to tilting of the instrument pier or
of the base in a direction at right angles to the
axis of the boom. When the coupling is direct,
overlapping of the record may, at times, be
troublesome. Romberg, when at the University
of Hawaii, devised a simple system for compensation of tilt. It consists of an oil coupling between the seismometer boom and the multiplying lever. The seismometer system was later
modified in the Coast and Geodetic Survey and
in this modified form was used in the shaking
table tests. Damping is magnetic and con-
veniently adjustable. Coupling is rather close
depending upon the viscosity of the oil and type
of multiplying lever used in the tilt compensat-
ing system.

Fig. 145. Galitzin horizontal seismograph with Hengler-Zoellner bifilar suspension, electromagnetic induction transducer, and electromagnetic damping. Hartmann and Braun long-period galvanometer, and recording drum with spring clock and double roller drive for rotation and gravity drive for sidewise translation.

— Courtesy H. Masing

Fig. 147. Aperiodical horizontal seismograph with galvanometric registration. After Prince B. Galitzin and Professor J. Wilip. Made by Hugo Masing factory for precision mechanics in Tartu, Estonia.

— Courtesy Cambridge Instrument Company

Fig. 146. Galitzin vertical-component seismograph as manufactured by the Cambridge Instrument Company and installed at Georgetown University after World War I.

— Courtesy H. Masing

Fig 148. Aperiodical vertical seismograph with compensation for temperature and galvanometric registration. After Prince B. Galitzin and Professor J. Wilip. Made by Hugo Masing factory for precision mechanics in Tartu, Estonia.

is not very sensitive to motion of the earth but which is connected to a variable reluctance transducer so that earthquake motion varies the magnetic flux through coils suitably wound and is recorded with a tremendously high magnification. These seismographs are unique in that two coils in each transducer are connected with two galvanometers of quite different period so that each component is equivalently two seismographs. This method of obtaining a very high magnification Benioff has applied to what he calls a strain seismograph. A very long rod is attached rigidly at one end to a support in the earth and is so suspended that it cannot move laterally. Between the other end of the rod and a similar fixed support

— Photo by U. S. Coast and Geodetic Survey

Fig. 149. Wenner seismometer. As in the Galitzin instrument, this seismometer is designed for galvanometric registration. The boom of the seismometer is hinged to a rigid column by very thin tempered brass hinges, in such a manner that it is free to oscillate in a horizontal plane. The outer end of the boom carries a coil, the axis of which is concentric with cylindrical pole pieces fixed to permanent magnets attached to the base of the instrument. The coil is free to move in the air gap between the pole pieces, and the plane of the coil is parallel to the lines of force of a strong, permanent, radial magnetic field. The terminals of the coil are closed through a sensitive galvanometer with suitable shunt in parallel. As the seismometer coil moves in a direction at right angles to this magnetic field, a current is induced in the coil and the branch circuits. These in turn produce an angular deflection of the galvanometer, which is much greater than the angular motion of the seismometer coil. Additional magnification and a continuous photographic record are obtained by reflecting a light beam from a mirror attached to the moving element of the galvanometer to a sheet of bromide paper attached to a suitable recorder. Damping is practically entirely electromagnetic and is easily and quickly adjustable by remote control by means of a shunt across the seismometer branch of the circuit. Nominal magnification varies from 1000 to 2000, depending upon the type of galvanometer used, the degree of damping, and the length of the optical lever. (This seismometer was manufactured by the R. Y. Ferner Company, formerly of Washington, D. C. The galvanometer is a standard instrument supplied by the Leeds and Northrup Company of Philadelphia.)

— Courtesy F. C. Henson Co., Pasadena

Fig. 151. The Benioff vertical component seismometer. A variable reluctance instrument electromagnetically damped.

— Courtesy F. C. Henson Co., Pasadena

Fig. 150. Short period Wood-Anderson torsion seismometer.

there is inserted a transducer similar to the one used on his other seismometers. In the seismograph we have a loose coupling, not between the earth and a weight, but between two parts of the earth's surface; yet the records made by this unique horizontal-component seismograph are very similar to those obtained with instruments of the pendulum type.

— Courtesy F. C. Henson Co., Pasadena

Fig. 152. Benioff horizontal component seismometer.

— Photo by Trefts

Fig. 153. Sprengnether horizontal component seismograph with electromagnetic recording and damping.

— Photo by Trefts

Fig. 154. Sprengnether vertical component seismograph with electromagnetic recording and damping.

Chapter XI

WHAT EARTHQUAKE RECORDS TELL US

Recording Mechanisms

Seismographic records of earthquakes are usually obtained by winding the record sheet about a drum or a pair of rollers. This drum is rotated at constant speed by clockwork and at the same time shifted sidewise by means of a screw so that the lines drawn in successive turns of the drum will not be superposed upon each other. As long as there is no relative motion between the pendulum of the seismograph and the earth the line will be straight, but it will be deflected to one side or the other by any relative movement. In order to permit the determination of the absolute time of any movement that is recorded, signals from an accurate timepiece are impressed upon the record every minute and every hour. Such a record sheet is called a *seismogram.*

Characteristics of Seismograms

In the older types of seismograms the record was very much compressed. Even the longer or more open time scales were usually not more rapid than four seconds to one millimeter. Thus it happened that the faster vibrations were not separated. In the record of the Crystal Springs earthquake of February 10, 1925, written at the Berkeley Station, the stylus was vibrating so rapidly that all of the soot was removed from the paper and the individual vibrations were thus merged into each other. In this case the periods were short, but in some earthquakes of more violent character the periods, even near the epicenter, are long. Thus, in the Cape Mendocino earthquake of January 22, 1923, the first movements began with an underlying period of twenty seconds. In that case the amplitudes were so large that the stylus was thrown from the paper on both components with the onset of the second group of waves. When the amplitudes are small, as they were in the record of the Crystal

— Photo by Rev. B. F. Doucette, S.J.

Fig. 155. Smoked paper recorder for horizontal
pendulums constructed at the Manila Observatory in 1907.

Springs earthquake, the vibrations may ride upon the larger waves
of the continuous earth movements known as microseisms. It is
easy to measure them in this case, but with the larger magnifications
the microseisms become more troublesome. In fact at times the
microseisms may be so large as to interlock and form almost a lace
pattern. It is then extremely difficult to pick up the earthquake
vibrations.

In the newer types of seismograms the time scale is much more

— Courtesy F. C. Henson Co., Pasadena

Fig. 156. Photographic recorder for the Benioff short-period
seismograph.

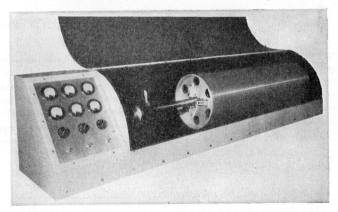

— Photo by Trefts

Fig. 157. Sprengnether triple recording drum.

open, covering one millimeter in one or two seconds. Nevertheless, the vibrations in some earthquakes at short distances may be so rapid as not to be resolved.

The Phases

The record of a near earthquake is generally characterized by the two distinct wave trains which we call $\overline{P}$ and $\overline{S}$. At intermediate distances an earthquake recorded on the older compressed scale shows two main parts — two series of smaller vibrations followed by very large vibrations. The older seismologists spoke of the first two wave trains as the preliminary portion of the record or the first preliminary and second preliminary phases; the large waves they called the principal phase. The first two of these are body waves, which travel through

Fig. 158. Smoked paper record of the Crystal Springs, California, earthquake, February 10, 1925, written by a Bosch-Omori seismograph at the Berkeley Station. Enlarged 10x.

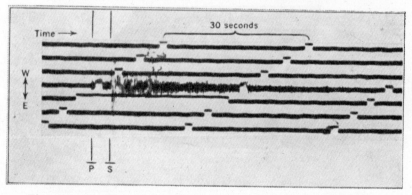

Fig. 159. Record of the Fern Glen, Missouri, earthquake of December 23, 1930, made by a Wood-Anderson torsion seismometer ($T =$ 2ₛ2) at the Florissant Station at a distance of eighteen miles.

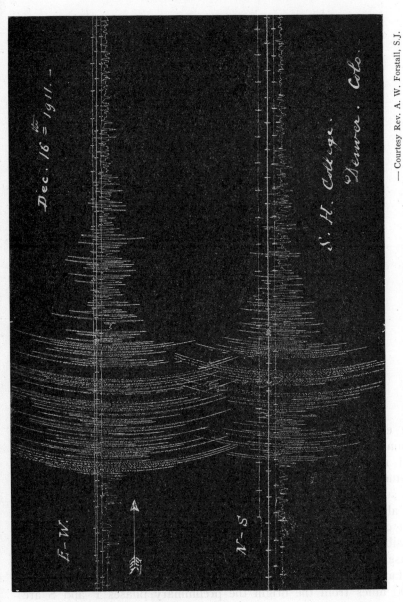

— Courtesy Rev. A. W. Forstall, S.J.

Fig. 160. Record of the Mexican earthquake of December 16, 1911,
written by the Wiechert seismograph at Regis College, Denver,
Colorado.

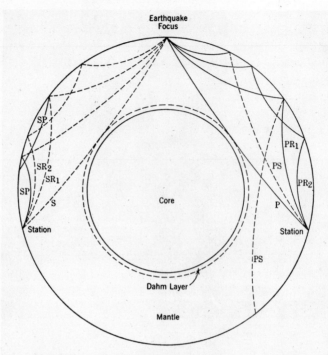

Fig. 161. Paths of some of the direct and reflected
body waves of the *P*-type (continuous lines) and the
S-type (broken lines).

the earth; the last are surface waves, which are propagated
around it. As the distance from the epicenter is increased, more
and more phases appear and the record made by a sensitive
seismograph may continue for hours, so that the waves recorded
on successive lines may overlap and interlock until they form
an almost undecipherable maze. If the earthquake is less violent or the magnification of the seismograph less great, it will be
possible to distinguish an entire series of successive phases. The P
phase will be followed by a series of reflections from the earth's
surface, as will also the S phase. At distances between 1500 and
5500 miles from the origin the preliminary phases P and S are
usually prominent. From 5500 miles onward to the antipodes the
records become very complicated. As we approach the distance of
about 7000 miles from the origin the amplitudes of the P phase
begin to decrease. Their energy becomes so small beyond 7200 miles

that only the most sensitive seismographs record the P waves. Clearly a shadow zone has been entered. As we progress onward through this shadow zone a new phase appears which is called P'. The shadow zone continues to a distance of about 10,000 miles. In the earthquake of June 26, 1924, which occurred in the far South Pacific, it happened that the two Canadian stations, Toronto and Ottawa, only 2 degrees apart, were critically situated to show to advantage the outer boundary of the shadow zone. At Toronto the P' phase was still very small, whereas at Ottawa it had become very large. Toronto was still in the shadow zone; Ottawa was in the

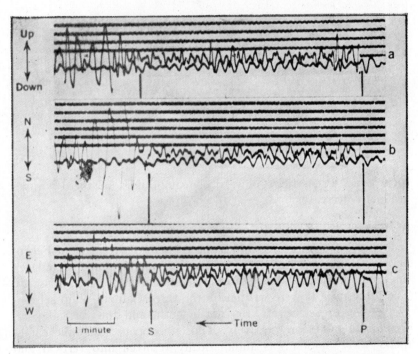

Fig. 162. Records of the P- and S-phases made by the three component Galitzin-Wilip seismographs at the Florissant Station (38°48′ N, 90°22′W) of the earthquake of Febraury 10, 1929, on the Gautemalan Deep at 13°5 N, 90°8 W, △ = 25°3. The Z- and N-components were, therefore, in the Plane of Propagation, and the E-component was normal to it. The interval between time marks is 30 seconds. Note the relative amplitudes of P near the right-hand end of the lines a, b, and c on the three components. Again it is seen that the P wave is longitudinal. The S waves toward the left-hand end of the same lines a, b, and c show transverse screwlike movement.

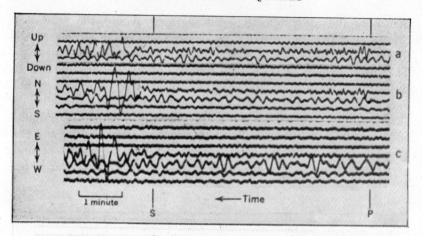

Fig. 163. Records of the *P*- and *S*-phases made by the three component Galitzin-Wilip seismographs at the Florissant Station, of the earthquake of February 15, 1929, at 13°.2 N, 90°.6 W on the Guatemalan Deep, $\triangle = 25°6$. The amplitudes were again resolved into longitudinal *Z*- and *N*-components and the transverse *E*-component. The record of the earthquake begins near the right-hand end of the lines marked *a*, *b*, and *c* and progresses toward the left. It will be noted that the *P*-motion is all longitudinal, there being no motion on *c* at *P*.

focal zone. From there onward the amplitudes of the P' waves gradually decrease.

Nature of the P and S Phases

Figure 162 shows the P and S phases of the earthquake of February 10, 1929, which occurred at a point on the Guatemalan Deep due south of the St. Louis University station at Florissant, Missouri. The three records were written by the three Galitzin-Wilip seismographs for the east-west, the north-south, and the vertical components of motion respectively. Thus it happened that the earthquake wave motion was automatically resolved into vertical and horizontal motion parallel to the plane of propagation — that is, the vertical plane through the center of the earth, the earthquake origin and the recording station — and the horizontal motion perpendicular to that plane. Examining the figure, we see that the east-west component shows scarcely any motion at the position marked P, the north-south component begins with a sharp northward impulse, and the vertical component begins with a very sharp upward impulse of larger amplitude. This is what we would expect if a longitudinal wave were arriving from the south and coming up at a steep angle. The S phase shows a rotation of the plane of vibration which corresponds to a non-polarized transverse wave.

Distance and Direction

With this general picture of the earthquake records before us we may ask ourselves how we can use them to determine the position of the epicenter of an earthquake when the beginning is not as sharp as in Figure 162. We have noticed in the records that there were two prominent phases P and S. These correspond, as we have seen, to two types of waves which started together and traveled at different speeds. Therefore, the interval between these two waves is a function of distance. Hence, to find the distance from the origin to the station we need only measure the time interval between the arrival of P and the arrival of S and consult an empirical table which connects this interval with the distance and with the time required for the P and S waves to travel that far.

Locating the Epicenter

If the *arcual distance* around the curved surface of the earth from the station to the earthquake and the *direction* of the origin from the recording station have been found from clear records such as those in Figure 162, it is a simple matter to measure off in the given direction on a good map if the distance is short, or on a globe if the distance is large. If the direction cannot be found from the records available at the station, then the epicenter may be anywhere on a circle whose arcual radius is the epicentral distance. If the distance from a second station is known, the two circles drawn about the two stations may be tangent to each other. Then the point of tangency is the approximate epicenter. If the two circles intersect, there are two possible solutions. If the distance from three stations is known, then the three circles will intersect at approximately one point, which is the epicenter.

Locating an epicenter is not so simple if the P and S phases are not recorded or cannot be identified, as is often the case at distances between 100 and 1000 miles and beyond 7000 miles. Then resort is had to other phases and to the method of successive approximation.

In order to facilitate the location of epicenters, *Science Service* of Washington, D. C. entered into an agreement with the United States

Fig. 164. Determining an epicenter at the Central Station of the Jesuit Seismological Association in St. Louis.

Coast and Geodetic Survey and the Jesuit Seismological Association to finance immediate telegraphic communication of earthquake data from important stations to Washington and to St. Louis on condition that each of the above-mentioned organizations make an independent solution of the epicenter and communicate the results to *Science Service*. If the locations found were in good agreement the geographical position of the epicenter was made available to the public. If the agreement was poor the result was held for further study when more data would be available. A reasonably complete list of all the epicenters in the world is published eventually in the *International Seismological Summary*.

The Inside of the Earth

About a half century ago Knott gave the first satisfactory theoretical interpretation of seismic waves through the body of the earth. Since then seismologists have seized upon every shred of evidence presented by earthquake waves in their effort to paint a reliable picture of the interior of our planet. The picture that has resulted is still blurred in many of its lines, sketchy in its details; but it is none the less interesting because we can trust the likeness as far as the painters' hands have gone in its development.

We are reasonably certain that the outer crust of the earth is like a layered cake or an onion in most places and is solid. Below the crust is a mantle of rock about 600 miles thick that is more rigid than steel and in which the speed of seismic waves increases rapidly with depth. Underneath this mantle lies an intermediate shell in which the speed of seismic waves is high and increases very slowly with depth. Then comes a transition into an inner core which acts on the seismic rays as a lens does on light, focussing them on the farther side of the earth and causing a shadow zone or dark belt to form around the bright spot. This core is some 4600 miles in diameter. Of what it is made we do not know, but we may venture

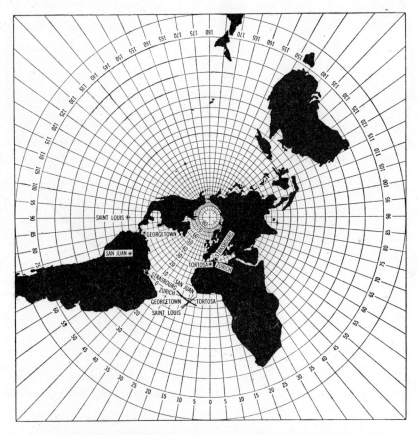

Fig. 165. Determination of the epicenter of the mid-Atlantic earthquake of May 19, 1933, by means of the Polar Stereographic Projection using geocentric latitudes. Base map by the Dominion Observatory, Ottawa, Canada.

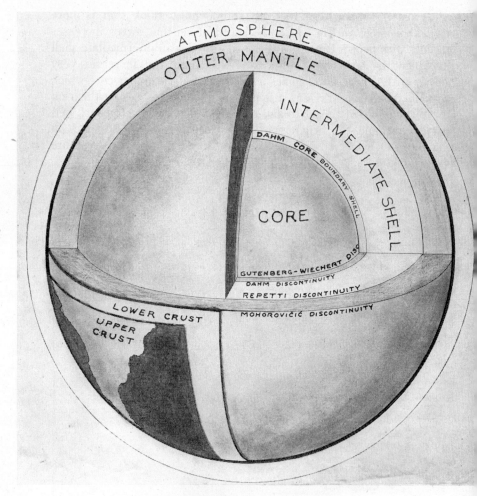

Fig. 166. Interior of the earth.

a plausible guess that an earth made up of a nickel-iron core surrounded by suitable layers of rock would probably behave very much like our actual earth.

Chapter XII

THE ENGINEER LOOKS AT EARTHQUAKES

Engineering Seismology Gets Off to a Late Start

In the late twenties and early thirties of the present century John R. Freeman agitated and campaigned for earthquake data that would help the engineer to design earthquake resistant structures. He spoke before scientific gatherings. He pleaded with the engineers themselves.[85]

Freeman would say that seismology had been developed almost exclusively along the lines of pure science and with little or no regard for the needs of the structural engineer. He wanted strong-motion seismographs that could be relied on to record the amplitude, period, and acceleration of destructive earthquake motion within the disturbed district. He called for precise measurement of the response of buildings and other structures to vibration.

Freeman deplored the fact that earthquake stresses played so small a part in the curriculum of American colleges of engineering and that there was no textbook in the English language on earthquake-resisting design. He said that thirteen out of fifteen prominent textbooks on structural design that he had examined did not even mention earthquake stress.

Government Takes a Hand

Largely as the result of the agitation of Freeman the interest of prominent United States Goverment officials was aroused in seismological engineering and the financial support of Congress was secured. Instruments were designed, built, and placed in operation in many parts of the country but particularly in California where more frequent earthquakes were expected.

Accelerographs

Rugged precision instruments suitable for the exact measurement of horizontal earthquake accelerations of nearly destructive to catas-

— Courtesy U. S. Coast and Geodetic Survey

Fig. 167. Accelerograph. Upper: side view; lower: top view. This instrument is used for recording photographically the horizontal and vertical motions of a building or of the ground in the vicinity of a moderate or destructive earthquake. It consists essentially of three accelerometers, a timing device, mechanisms for starting and stopping the apparatus automatically, and a photographic recorder, all of which remain inactive unless set into operation by the earthquake. The accelerometer is the element which is sensitive to ground motion. In reality it is a small seismometer having a natural period of one-tenth second. The moving element or vane is heavily damped by means of a cobalt-steel magnet. Light from a battery lamp is reflected from a mirror attached to the accelerometer vane and brought to focus on the photographic paper attached to the recorder. The three accelerometers are mounted with their axles at right angles to one another, the light from the three mirrors being brought to focus on the drum in the same horizontal line. It is thus possible to record three components of the motion simultaneously. The ampli-

trophic intensity were designed by Wenner of the United States Bureau of Standards and improved by McComb of the United States Coast and Geodetic Survey. A similar instrument for the vertical component acceleration was designed by McComb.

These instruments were built in considerable numbers and mounted so as to record photographically all three components of the acceleration in a fairly large number of buildings.

The first important set of records were those of the Long Beach earthquake of March 10, 1933, secured at Long Beach seventeen miles from the epicenter, at Vernon thirty-three miles away and in Los Angeles thirty-seven miles distant from the epicenter. The records were sent to the Washington office of the United States Coast and Geodetic Survey for measurement and interpretation. At Long Beach where considerable damage was done by the earthquake there was a ground acceleration slightly less than one-quarter of the acceleration of gravity in waves of three-tenths second period.

When the series of Helena, Montana, earthquakes began October 18, 1935, a set of these strong-motion accelerographs was hurried by truck from the Pacific Coast and set up in Helena. Usually the beginning of the earthquake motion is relied upon to start the recording mechanism and in consequence is lost from the record. But on one occasion an earthquake occurred while the recorder was still operating because of a previous shock and was completely registered.

---

tude of the recorded motion is practically proportional to the ground acceleration for periods of the ground which are greater than about one-third second. Each accelerometer is equipped with a low-magnification attachment which furnishes an additional record. This insures obtaining readable records from both moderate and severe earthquakes. The automatic starting device consists of an oil-damped conical pendulum, which closes an electric contact if it moves in any horizontal direction by a small amount thereby operating a relay which closes other circuits, the action of which starts the driving motor of the recorder, releases the brake on the time-marking clock, and turns on the battery lamp. After a short time the recorder and clock stop automatically and the light is extinguished unless the earthquake motion still persists. The recorder is designed for about 10 automatic operations before the paper is exhausted. Forty of these accelerographs, in addition to other types of strong-motion instruments, are now operated by the Survey in various seismic regions of the United States. The results obtained with instruments of this type are being used in connection with the design of earthquake-resistant buildings and other structures.

Fig. 168. Detail of accelerometer shown in Figure 167. The accelerometers as used on the accelerograph were designed in their original form by Dr. Frank Wenner, of the National Bureau of Standards. The instruments have been greatly modified since then by the Coast and Geodetic Survey. The instrument as used at present consists of a rectangular loop of copper pivoted eccentrically about one of its longer sides and coupled to a supporting frame by a helical spring so adjusted as to provide a natural period of 0.1 second to the system. The mirror, which is used in photographic registration, is a planoconvex lens silvered on the plane side and is attached to the vane. The side of the loop which is opposite the pivoted side is flattened into a vane and is free to oscillate in a narrow air gap between the pole pieces of a powerful cobalt-steel magnet, thus providing magnetic damping, which is adjustable over a wide range by a sliding shunt with indicator dial. An adjustable-base-line mirror is mounted on the suspension bracket at the same elevation as the van mirror. A zero adjuster permits of easy and accurate adjustment of the light spot to any position on the face of the recorder. By a slight modification of the base the suspension system is mounted in such a manner as to serve as a vertical component. In practice three of these instruments are mounted close together on a common base and by suitable arrangement of prisms or stellite mirrors two of the accelerometers serve as horizontal components at right angles to each other and the third as a vertical component, all recording simultaneously on the same drum. A second mirror (facing upward on the horizontal component) is mounted on the axis of rotation of the vane and is directly below a

From the accelerograms both the velocity and the displacement are derived by mathematical means.

As a response to the demand of engineers that measurements of earthquake motion be made on the upper floors of buildings as well as in their basements, accelerographs were set up in the basement and on the thirteenth floor of a thirteen-story building in San Jose, California. The records of the Nevada earthquake of June 25, 1933, showed that the acceleration was very much greater on the thirteenth floor than it was in the basement. Consequently it became a common practice of the Survey to place instruments on several floors of large buildings.

Besides these short-period accelerographs a fair number of long-period, photographic displacement meters were built and installed in California and elsewhere.

A strong-motion seismograph recording on smoked glass by means of a stylus was designed by the late Arthur J. Weed of the University of Virginia. Instruments of this type were installed at a number of places in California.

All of these strong-motion seismographs have been recording earthquakes for a sufficient number of years to show the general trend. And the data[86] concerning frequencies, accelerations, and displacements derived from the Long Beach (1933), Nevada (1933), Eureka (1934), El Centro (1934), Helena (1935), Cape Mendocino (1938), El Centro (1940), and many other earthquakes are utilized by engineers, architects, and insurance men. The experience derived from these measurements has led to modifications of the building codes and to better practice in designing structures.

Nevertheless, the engineers were not satisfied because strong earthquakes were too few and the recording instruments were too scattered to furnish immediate answers to the questions posed.

---

reflecting prism attached to the bracket. The amplitude of the motion of the spot of light from the mirror is a function of the angle of inclination of the mirror to the axis of rotation. In practice the mirror is set at such an angle that the amplitude of motion of its spot will be about one-seventh that of the normal spot. By using such a device there is little chance of losing any record from the most severe earthquakes.

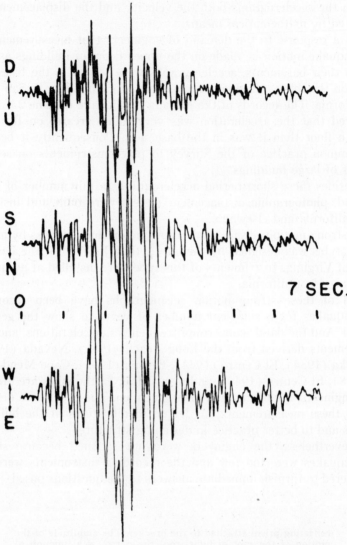

Fig. 169. Section of an accelerograph record as recorded by a three-component accelerograph at Helena, Montana, on October 31, 1935. Paper speed about 11mm. per second.

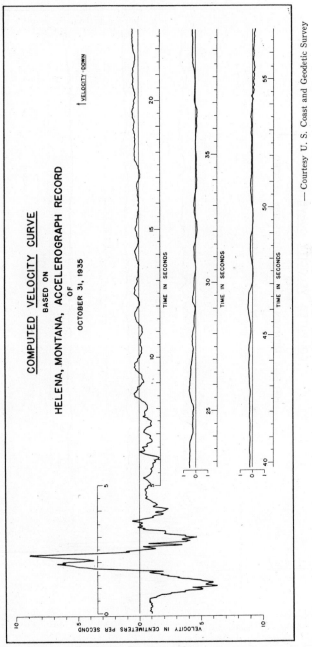

COMPUTED VELOCITY CURVE

BASED ON

HELENA, MONTANA, ACCELEROGRAPH RECORD

OF

OCTOBER 31, 1935

— Courtesy U. S. Coast and Geodetic Survey

Fig. 170. A.

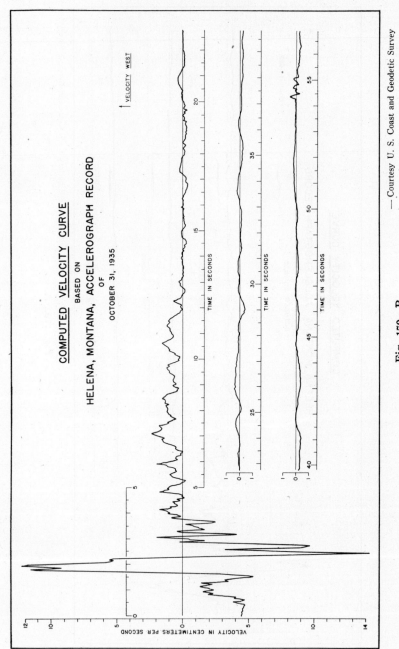

Fig. 170. B.

— Courtesy U. S. Coast and Geodetic Survey

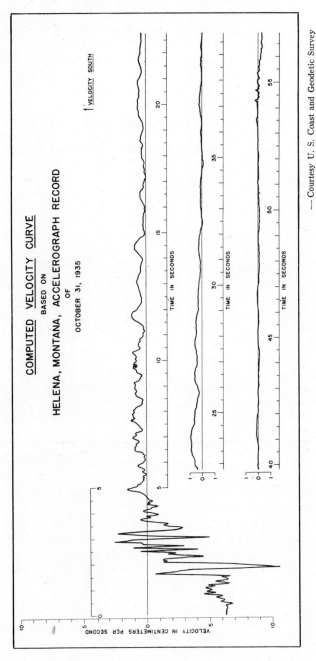

COMPUTED VELOCITY CURVE
BASED ON
HELENA, MONTANA, ACCELEROGRAPH RECORD
OF
OCTOBER 31, 1935

VELOCITY SOUTH

TIME IN SECONDS

VELOCITY IN CENTIMETERS PER SECOND

Fig. 170. C.

—Courtesy U. S. Coast and Geodetic Survey

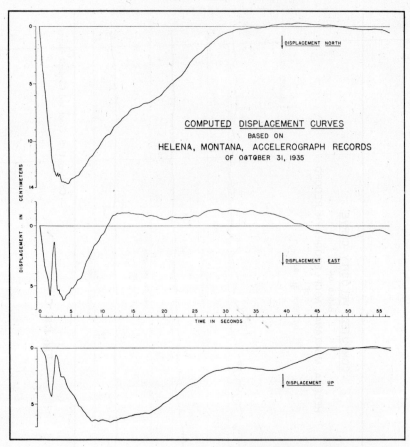

— Courtesy U. S. Coast and Geodetic Survey

Fig. 171.

— Courtesy U. S. Coast and Geodetic Survey

Fig. 172. U. S. Coast and Geodetic Survey displacement meter. This instrument was designed primarily for the registration of horizontal displacements of the ground in the vicinity of a destructive earthquake. It consists of two oil-damped, horizontal pendulums, each having a steady mass of one pound mounted at right angles to each other and designed for unit magnification. Provision is made for photographic registration on two drums having a common axle, the drums being driven by a battery motor. The speed of the photographic paper to be attached is about 7mm./sec. Light from one galvanometer lamp is directed toward two small mirrors mounted on the axes of rotation of the pendulums and after reflection is brought to focus on the faces of the drums. Cylindrical lenses bring the images down to sharp points. The light is also directed toward mirrors on a time-marking clock (which operates eclipsing device) and after reflection, these rays are brought to focus on the two drums. Time marks at about ½ second intervals are thus placed on the records. On each boom is mounted a short piece of platinum wire pointing downward. If the boom is displaced through a small angle in either direction, this platinum wire makes contact with a second platinum wire which is mounted on the armature of a sensitive relay. As soon as contact is made, an electric current flows through the contact and the coil of a relay. This relay closes other electric circuits which light the galvanometer lamp, start the driving motor, and cause the timing clocks to begin functioning. At the same time a signal device (which may, for convenience, be remote from the displacement meters) is operated. The recorder continues to function for 1 1/3 revolutions, after which it stops, the timing clock stops, and the lamp is extinguished; then the whole apparatus is reset in its original condition. If and when the platinum wires again come in contact it starts again and the above cycle is repeated. These repetitions may follow each other immediately or after a lapse of hours or days. It is intended that the signal device shall warn the operator that the apparatus has functioned. The entire apparatus, except the battery, is self-contained and occupies a space of 24 x 40 x 44 inches.

— Courtesy U. S. Coast and Geodetic Survey

Fig. 173. The Weed Strong-Motion Seismograph. This instrument is designed for the registration of accelerations of the ground and parts of buildings in the vicinity of and during the time of a major earthquake. It consists of a cylindrical steady mass of about 5 to 7 pounds mounted on three steel wires, the whole forming an inverted pendulum. The wire supports are attached rigidly to a common base and near the edge of one end of the steady mass, the system having a period of about 0.2 second. Oil damping is secured by means of a perforated cylinder mounted directly below the steady mass and dipping in an oil cup.

Registration of two horizontal components of the motion of the steady mass is secured by means of two mechanical multiplying levers. One end of each lever is attached to the frame of the instrument and the other carries a stylus. The lever is coupled to the steady mass in such a manner as to give a static magnification of about 7. Each stylus rests against a smoked glass plate. This glass plate is given motion of translation by means of a spring clock which pulls the plate along in a horizontal plane above the stylusses.

Automatic starting and stopping is accomplished by means of an electromagnetic device which is operated by means of pendulum starting devices. The entire apparatus is self-contained and occupies a space of approximately 8 x 8 x 20 inches.

Chapter XIII

ENGINEERING SEISMOLOGY

The shaking in an earthquake is a very complex motion. This had been inferred from the accounts of eye witnesses as well as from many of the destructive effects observed. However, the strong-motion earthquake records described in the last chapter show that earthquake motion is even more complicated than was thought.

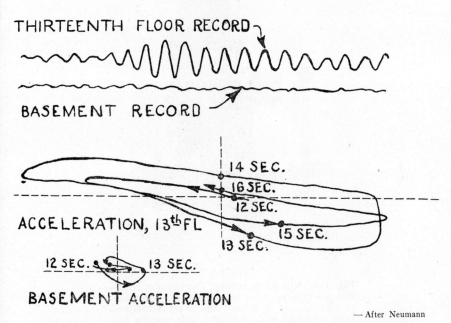

— After Neumann

Fig. 174. Part of the strong motion record of the western Nevada earthquake of June 25, 1933, written by accelerographs in the basement and on the thirteenth floor of the Bank of America building in San Jose, California, together with diagrams of the resultant horizontal accelerations during an interval of four seconds from the 12th to the 16th.

Earthquake Motion in Upper Stories of Buildings

The records of strong-motion seismographs installed by the United States Coast and Geodetic Survey in the basement and on the top floor of the thirteen-story Bank of America building in San Jose, Califorina, showed so great a difference between the motion of the top of the building and that at the bottom that engineers and architects called for experimental studies of the vibration of structures in addition to the observation of earthquake effects.

Vibration Measurements

Some studies of this kind had been made in the past. Thus as far back as 1911–1912 Hall[87] designed a three-component portable seis-

— Photo by U. S. Coast and Geodetic Survey

Fig. 175. Vibration meter. The torsion vibration meter is used for measuring natural periods of vibration of buildings and other structures. It is equipped with a copper vane, torsion suspension, and adjustable magnetic damping, and is designed for convenience of operation in the field. Vanes of different dimensions permit operation at different static magnifications and different frequency ranges. It is similar in principle to the Wood-Anderson seismometer.

— Photo by U. S. Coast and Geodetic Survey

Fig. 176. Vibration Meter Recorder. This recorder is driven by a synchronous motor or by a six-volt direct-current motor having different gear ratios for obtaining different paper speeds. Convenient electrical outlets and switches make it possible to control from one station two or more of these recorders operating simultaneously on different floors of the building, the time marks being simultaneous on all records. Recorders of this type have been used extensively in the building vibration program of the Coast and Geodetic Survey in California.

mograph and measured the vibrations due to street traffic in a number of buildings in the San Francisco Bay region and in 1914–1917 the vibrations of the Sather Tower at successive stages in its construction. The same instrument was used by Byerly[88] in 1931 to measure the natural period of vibration of sixteen tall buildings in San Francisco. The vibrations in the latter case were excited by the wind. In England in 1913 traffic induced vibrations were measured[89] in the clock tower at Westminster and in St. Paul's, London. In the years immediately following the first World War, Omori in Japan designed portable instruments and measured traffic and wind vibrations of tall chimneys, of a radio tower, of bridges, piers, and tall buildings, as did Ishimoto in the middle twenties.

The United States Coast and Geodetic Survey in 1934 undertook vibration studies[90] in California on a far more extensive scale. So many *water tanks* were damaged or destroyed in the Long Beach and other earthquakes in California that the United States Coast

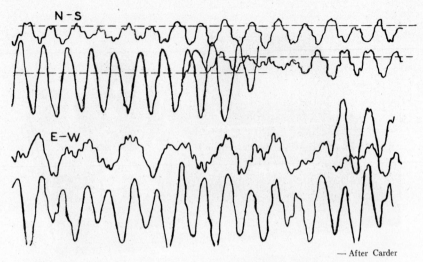

— After Carder

Fig. 177. Vibrogram of the Standard Sanitary Products Company Water Tower, San Pablo, California, indicating three types of vibration, T = 2.6 seconds, T = 1.33 second, T = 0.35 second.

and Geodetic Survey centered much of its attention in the earlier vibration work on these structures. The vibrations caused by wind pressure on tank towers of various types, — wooden tanks on steel frames, tanks on and in buildings, and independent tank structures, — were investigated. Several distinct periods of vibration were usually observed. For a tank in San Pablo these were interpreted as (1) the fundamental period of the tower, 1.33 seconds, (2) the period of the water oscillating in the tank, 2.6 seconds, (3) the period of torsional vibrations of the tower, 0.35 seconds. In 1934 and 1935 systematic studies of the vibrations caused in *tall buildings* by wind were undertaken by the United States Coast and Geodetic Survey. Each building was found to sway with characteristic periods of translation and of torsion which lay for the greatest part between two-tenths second and two seconds; the torsional period being smaller than the translational. However, there was doubt as to the free character of these periods — whether these vibrations were merely *excited* or were *forced* by the gusts of wind.

Shaking Table Experiments

Two lines of research were undertaken to secure the requisite information. Ruge[91] in the Civil Engineering Laboratory of the

Massachusetts Institute of Technology studied the behavior of model water tank towers and other structures under vibrations that similated earthquakes. With light from a stroboscope he slowed down the tank tower movements until they could be observed with ease. With a shaking table controlled by an electric eye which followed an integrated Long Beach earthquake curve he subjected his models to destructive earthquake conditions.

Shaking tables had been used before to study the earthquake resisting properties of wall panels, chimneys, piers, and other structures at Stanford University by Jacobsen[92] in the late twenties, at California Institute of Technology by Martel, and still earlier by Bierer and Parker[93] in 1911, and by Alvarez[94] in 1925 at the University of California in Berkeley. But none of these investigators had used a *facsimile* of an actual earthquake as the source of table vibrations as Ruge did.

The second line of research that was undertaken by the United States Coast and Geodetic Survey was the artificial vibration of structures.

Shaking Water Tank Towers

Water tank towers were caused to vibrate in two ways. The first method was to shake the tie rods until the whole tower was vibrat-

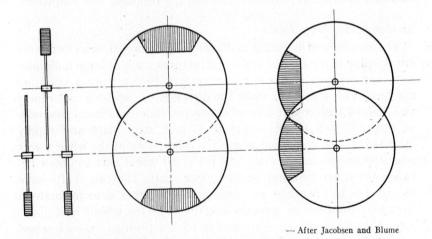

— After Jacobsen and Blume

Fig. 178. Vibrating machine. Diagram illustrating the arrangement of the three wheels and of the eccentric weights to secure balance of forces in one direction and maximum force in the direction normal to it.

— Courtesy U. S. Coast and Geodetic Survey

Fig. 179. More compact building oscillator used by the U. S.
Coast and Geodetic Survey in building vibration work.

ing. These vibrations were recorded by the same vibration meters as
were used in the wind tests. The second method was to attach a rope
to some part of the tower, pull the rope until the desired deflection
was obtained, and then to release the tower suddenly. Instruments
mounted in selected positions recorded the resulting free vibrations.

Shaking Machine Tests

The methods of inducing artificial vibrations just described were
not possible in the case of massive structures, such as large buildings,
dams, or bridges. Hence it was necessary to construct a vibrating
machine. This was done under the direction of Jacobsen and Blume
at Stanford University. The vibrating machine consisted essentially
of three 30-inch wheels made of ¼-inch steel plate and rigidly
mounted on two shafts one above the other. Two of the wheels were
mounted on the lower shaft and the third wheel was mounted between the other two, but on the upper shaft. The two shafts were
mounted in ball bearings and were geared together so as to rotate at
the same speed but in opposite directions. To the wheels lead plates
were bolted in such amounts and in such a position on each wheel
that their centrifugal forces were opposed and balanced when vertically over each other and reinforced each other at either side. The
weight of lead on the upper wheel is twice that on each of the two

lower wheels so that the same unbalanced force was applied to each shaft and a simple harmonic force was transmitted through the frame to the building.

When in use the frame was rigidly braced between two structural units, or bolted securely to the structure to be tested. The shafts were driven by a direct current motor and V-belt until the highest desired speed was attained. The belt was then removed and the wheels allowed to coast to a stop. During the interval of about five minutes from the removal of the belt until the machine stops, the frequency of the harmonic force impulses is continually decreasing, and vibration recorders set up at suitable locations in the structure are obtaining a continuous record of the amplitude of the forced vibrations of the whole structure or of that part of the structure in which they are placed. For simultaneous measurements of the vibrations in different parts of a building or on different floors the Benioff reluctance seismographs and field recorder were found very useful. The Benioffs are similar to the seismic prospecting systems that will

— Courtesy U. S. Coast and Geodetic Survey

Fig. 180. Benioff recording units for the four-channel portable seismograph.

Fig. 181. Pickup unit of the Benioff four-channel
portable seismograph.

Fig. 182. Galvanometer block in the
Benioff four-channel recorder.

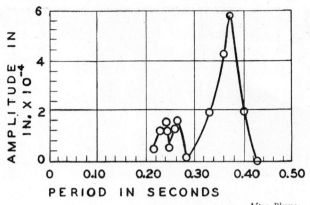

— After Blume

Fig. 183. Resonance curve for the thirteenth floor of the Bank of America Building, San Jose, California.

be discussed in a later chapter but were specially designed for strong-motion work and have only four channels.

The first shaking machine did not exert enough force to excite the natural frequencies of the more massive structures, and therefore a larger machine with all three wheels on the same level was constructed in the shops at Stanford University.

As the machine slows down, the frequency of the vibrations grad-

— Courtesy U. S. Coast and Geodetic Survey

Fig. 184. Neumann-Labarre vibration meter.

— Courtesy U. S. Coast and Geodetic Survey

Fig. 185. Patterson ground shaker in use with supporting
framework and weights.

ually decreases. When the frequency of the vibrations reaches a
value equal to that of free oscillations of the structure, resonance
occurs and the recorded amplitudes build up rapidly to a maximum
and then decrease again. This rise and fall of amplitude may happen
several times in each run because the structure may have several

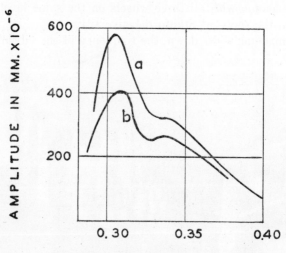

— After Kohler

Fig. 186. Resonance curves of the ground in the
Leine Valley near Gottingen: (a) at 480 meters
distance from the shaking machine, (b) at 590
meters on the opposite side of the Leine River.

free periods; and not only the fundamental frequencies but also harmonics may be excited. Comparison of the shaker tests with the wind vibration records showed that water tank towers and other tall structures oscillate at their fundamental natural frequencies.

— Courtesy U. S. Coast and Geodetic Survey

Fig. 187a. Patterson vertical component vibration meter, magnetically damped.

Ground Period

A further problem that has troubled both seismologists and engineers is whether the massive layers in the crust of the earth and even the sedimentary rocks, the soils, and individual topographic features, such as bluffs, hills, and valley fills, have natural periods of vibration of their own. Will they resonate to impulses of the right frequency? Is a building and the ground on which it rests a coupled system which may be in resonance? It might be disastrous if building, ground, and earthquake were all in resonance.

Experiments[95] near Göttingen, Germany, seemed to indicate that the ground did have resonant frequencies of its own. The attention

Fig. 187b. Patterson vertical component
vibration meter with cover removed and
damping mechanism opened.

of the United States Coast and Geodetic Survey was directed to the
problem by observations with the shaker in the basements of tall
buildings, as for example in the Bank of America Building in San
Jose, California, where the ground and not the building was set in
vibration. A new and more powerful shaking machine was developed
by Patterson[96] somewhat similar to the building shaker used by
Blume. Vibration meters of higher sensitivity were needed than
those used in building vibration measurements. The Neumann-
Labarre horizontal component and the Patterson vertical component
vibration meters, magnifying the ground motion 10,000 times, were
found to be very satisfactory. The Benioff four-channel pickup and
recorder system was found useful for simultaneous recording of
near and distant stations.

The following conclusions may be drawn from the five years of experimentation, 1935–1940. First, the ground generally has many natural periods of vibration which vary from place to place and are usually different in different directions at any given place. Second, most ground resonances cover a fairly wide band of frequencies, thus differing from building resonances which are usually sharp and well defined. Third, resonances are more pronounced on soft, marshy, or made ground and less pronounced on solid rock. Fourth, a structure, such as a building, dam, or tower, forms, together with the ground on which it is built, a coupled elastic system in which vibratory energy is readily transferred to resonating parts. Vibrations induced by a shaking machine in the Hollywood Storage Building were picked up in the ground outside as far away as 1.2 miles. However, the natural periods of the ground seem too numerous to make it practicable so to design buildings that they will avoid all resonance with the ground.

Chapter XIV

SEISMOLOGICAL ENGINEERING

An entirely new field of engineering is being developed to deal with industrial problems that arise from man-made earthquakes, such as quarry blasts, trip hammer blows, vibrating machinery, and highway and railway traffic, and with the laboratory study of those properties of rocks that may come into play in either natural or artificial earthquakes.

Seismic Effects of Quarry Blasting

The detonation of explosives is the fastest, most efficient, and most economical method of quarrying rock for the manufacture of lime and cement, for smelting, for road metal, for concrete, and for many other uses. Now a quarry cannot be opened at random anywhere. The commercial success of a quarry depends on a number of factors. It must deliver the type of rock for which there is demand. The rock must be readily accessible without too much stripping of overburden. The market must be sufficiently near so that haulage will not be excessive. In most cases the requirements as to the chemical constitution and physical properties of the rock are rather severe. Hence a good quarry represents an important asset and usually involves a considerable investment.

Naturally the employees of the quarry wish to live near their work. Hence they build their homes in the vicinity. These men and their families are interested in the quarry and consider its operation a blessing.

Gradually, however, the community grows. The neighborhood becomes a residential district. Real estate promotion begins. Merchants and other people are attracted who have no direct interest in the quarry. The quarry blasts disturb their families and gradually take on the aspects of a nuisance in their minds. Someone discovers structural cracks in his house. He is perturbed and talks to his neighbors about it. They also find cracks in their houses. Settling

Fig. 188. Taylor-Macelwane portable seismograph used at St. Louis
University for the measurement of quarry blasts.

and differential movement in the course of years cause structural
cracks to appear in nearly all dwellings.

Sometimes there are special geological conditions, such as fire clay
under porous soil, that favor differential movement between the
parts of a building. Cracks are thus widened to form gaping fissures.
The differential movement may be so great as, in extreme cases, to
endanger the stability of the structure. Someone suggests that the
quarry blasts are the cause of the cracking. Everybody listens for
the blasts. The houses shake. The windows rattle. The owners become convinced that the quarry is shaking down their houses. Liti-
gation starts; and the war is on to put the quarry out of business.

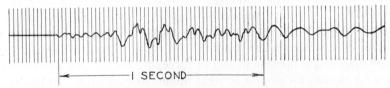

Fig. 189. Portable seismograph record of a quarry blast near St.
Louis. The distance from shot to seismograph was 1900 feet. Note
the separation of longitudinal and transverse phases at this short
distance.

Until the development of modern portable seismographs with
high sensitivity and high-speed timing and recording there was no
accurate means of determining the strength of the vibrations set up
by quarry blasts. Courts and juries were at a loss to determine

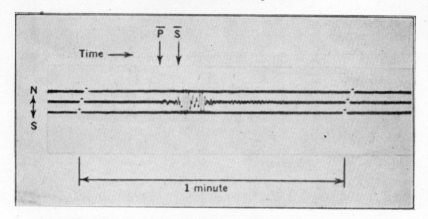

Fig. 190. Record of a quarry blast near St. Louis made by a Wood-Anderson seismograph ($T = 1\overset{.}{.}8$) at a distance of 14 miles.

whether the vibrations transmitted through the ground from blasts were actually causing damage to the home of a litigant.

At this juncture the quarries appealed to the geophysicists to measure the vibrations caused by their blasts. This was done. But the question that immediately presented itself was: How strong must a vibration be to cause damage to an average structure?

At the request of the quarry industry the United States Bureau of Mines in 1930 began a systematic program of experimental research to evaluate the effects of seismic waves from quarry blasts on buildings and other typical structures. A geophysical section was formed in the Bureau of Mines and development work was begun. By 1935 suitable seismometers, recorders, shaking table and field techniques had been perfected so that the actual testing of structures could begin. The seismometers were of the capacitative electromagnetic type designed to operate in sets of three, one for vertical motion and two for horizontal motion at right angles to each other. In the final design the seismometer consisted of two insulated conducting plates fixed to the frame with a third conducting plate suspended on hinges so as to move freely between the other two. The two outside plates moved with the ground under the influence of the blast vibrations while the inertia of the suspended plate tended to keep it stationary. Since the two spaces between pairs of plate faces were made to act as two radio condensers in a pair of coupled vacuum tube oscillators, the current in the system varied with the displacement of the ground, alternating rapidly with the blast vibrations. The alternating current was fed through a third vacuum tube and thus rectified into direct current which was then led through a connecting wire into a Duddel-type oscillograph. A mirror on the oscillograph deflected a beam of light whose movement was photographed. Twelve oscillographs were arranged side by side so that records from twelve seismometers could be made simultaneously on the same film. The vibrations are timed by means of lines crossing the record every one-hundredth of a second. These lines are produced by a beam of light reflected from a vibrating tuning fork. Thus the frequency and amplitude of the vibration due to the quarry blast could be measured. From these two, the acceleration could be derived.

During the five years from the summer of 1935 to the fall of 1940, hundreds of tests were made at twenty-eight stone quarries situated in eleven states, in mines, and in twenty residential structures of various kinds. The blasts that were measured followed regular quarry practice. The charges of explosive varied from 1.5 to 42,000 pounds. The distances at which the blast vibrations were measured ranged from one hundred feet to two miles.

From this mass of data Thoenen[97] and Windes drew the following conclusions. First, the seismic vibrations that are generated by quarry blasting in accordance with customary practice produce no greater displacements of the ground and of residential structures than those caused by normal living activities within the house or ordinary traffic conditions outside. Second, defining the beginning of damage as the cracking of average plaster on wooden lath, an acceleration in the blast vibrations equal to that of gravity is a practical index of damage. Third, it was not found possible to damage residential structures at usual distances by means of normal quarry blasts, the measured accelerations never exceeding a very small percentage of gravity. Fourth, in order actually to produce damage and thus establish whether 100 per cent of gravity is a reliable index for the beginning of damage, it was found necessary to vibrate the structures by means of a shaking machine, or to set off an abnormal charge of explosive almost under the house. Taking the percentage of gravity as ten times the displacement times the square of the frequency of vibration — or in other words, supposing the vibrations to be simple harmonic — Thoenen and Windes blocked off the tabulated results into *safe, caution, damage* values as follows:

Displacement in inches	Frequency in Cycles Per Second						
	2	4	6	8	10	15	20
	Acceleration in Percentage of Gravity						
0.24	10	38	86	150	240	540	960
0.22	9	35	79	140	220	500	880
0.20	8	32	72	130	200	450	800
0.18	7.2	29	65	120	180	410	720
0.16	6.4	26	58	100	160	360	640
0.14	5.6	22	50	90	140	320	560
0.12	4.8	19	43	77	120	270	480
0.10	4.0	16	36	64	100	220	400
0.08	3.2	13	29	51	80	180	320
0.06	2.4	10	22	38	60	130	240
0.04	1.6	6	14	26	40	90	160
0.02	0.8	3	7	13	20	40	80
0.01	0.4	1.6	3.6	6.4	10	20	40
0.008	0.32	1.3	2.9	5.1	8	20	30
0.006	0.24	1.0	2.2	3.8	6	10	20
0.004	0.16	0.6	1.4	2.6	4	9	20
0.002	0.08	0.3	0.7	1.3	2	4	8
0.001	0.04	0.16	0.36	0.6	1	2	4
0.0008	0.03	0.13	0.29	0.5	0.8	2	3
0.0006	0.02	0.10	0.22	0.4	0.6	1	2
0.0004	0.02	0.06	0.14	0.26	0.4	1	1.6
0.0002	0.01	0.03	0.07	0.13	0.2	0.4	0.8
0.0001	0.00	0.02	0.04	0.06	0.1	0.2	0.4

☐ SAFE   ▓ CAUTION   ▨ DAMAGE

Damage From Air Blast

In the course of the tests on the seismic effects of quarry blasting the question of possible damage resulting from air blasts often presented itself. Although the air waves from quarry blasts were often recorded, the apparatus was not designed for the measurement of air blasts and their investigation was only begun after the research on seismic effects had been completed.

Instead of seismometers it was necessary to have microphones suited to the measurement of air blasts. Also it was essential that the recorder be sensitive to very-low-frequency impulses, and even to sustained pressure. Suitable apparatus was developed in 1940.

The tests made between 1940 and 1942 showed that danger of damage from air blast in the usual quarry shot is insignificant. The first damage that occurs is the failure of window glass. Window panes will crack or break when the maximum pressure pulse in the air blast reaches one to two pounds per square inch. The air blast from large quarry shots produced maximum pressures much less than one pound per square inch. Drill-hole shots cause pressures of about 0.01 pound to the square inch and seam shots about 0.1 pound to the square inch. In fact with drill-hole or block-hole shots it was found to be impossible to cause air blast damage.

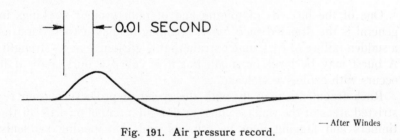

Fig. 191. Air pressure record.

— After Windes

The character of the seismic record of a quarry blast is usually quite different from that of the corresponding record of the air blast; the latter being much simpler and building up to maximum pressure much more rapidly.

It was found by Birkenhauer and Walter at St. Louis University that the seismic record even at short distances shows the separation of the longitudinal and transverse waves.

Chapter XV

ROCK BURSTS AND OVERSTRAIN

One of the hazards of mining and of underground workings in general is the dreaded *rock burst*. Spalding defined a rock burst as a sudden failure of rock under strain that is greater than its strength. A burst may be large or small, but it is called a burst only if it occurs with explosive violence.

Rock fragments may fly with the speed of projectiles from restricted areas of the walls, ceiling, or floor of a tunnel or drift, or the timbers and lagging may be crushed and the opening suddenly closed. Fatalities often result.

Rock bursts are a constant menace in copper mines of the Lake Superior region, in the nickel and gold mines of northern Ontario, in the Kolar gold mines of India, in the Witwatersrand mines of South Africa, and elsewhere. All of these mines are deep. But great depth is not a necessary condition for the occurrence of rock bursts.

Fig. 192. Complete equipment assembled at Ottawa for the seismological laboratory at Lake Shore Mines, Kirkland Lake, Ontario. Heiland geophone in the middle.

They are present in the coal mines of the United States, in the water tunnels of New York, and in the marble quarries of Vermont.

Bucky[98] summarized the conditions necessary for a rock burst as the presence of: (1) One or more *free faces;* (2) Rock that is very *elastic,* — that exerts a strong restoring force which grows proportionately greater the more the rock is strained; (3) *Overstrain* so great that the internal stresses exceed the strength of the rock.

The strain energy that is released in a rock burst is often enormous. A rock burst[99] in the Lake Shore Mines at Kirkland Lake, Ontario, December 27, 1938, was recorded not only by the Benioff seismograph at the Dominion Observatory in Ottawa 279 miles away, but also at Weston College near Boston which is 581 miles from Kirkland Lake. Hodgson[100] states that fourteen rock bursts in the Lake Shore Mines were recorded at Ottawa between December, 1938, and August, 1943.

Fig. 193. Heiland geophone with the
outer case removed.

Many engineering procedures have been proposed to predict and control rock bursts at least to the extent of safeguarding the miners. However, the only method that promises reliable prediction is the seismological one.

At the invitation of Lake Shore Mines the Dominion Observatory at Ottawa undertook an extended program of research under the

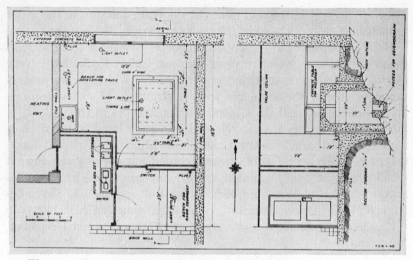

Fig. 194. Plan and elevation of the seismological laboratory at Lake Shore Mines, Kirkland Lake, Ontario.

direction of Doctor E. A. Hodgson and with the assistance of Mr. Zack E. Gibbs. At the surface at Kirkland Lake a seismological laboratory was established in 1939 and equipped with a Heiland geophone, a recording camera designed and constructed by the Heiland Research Corporation of Denver, Colorado, a National Standard HRO radio receiver for the reception and recording of time signals, and a chronometer to place a mark on the record every

Fig. 195. Heiland geophone emplaced in cement; surface seismographic laboratory at Lake Shore Mines.

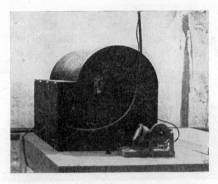

Fig. 196. Photographic recorder on the pier table over the seismograph emplacement in the seismographic laboratory at Lake Shore Mines. The entrance to the seismograph chamber may be seen in the left end of the concrete recorder table.

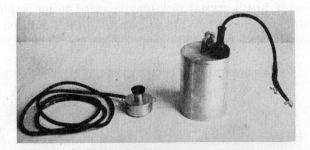

Fig. 197. Brush crystal detector and second Heiland geophone for use down in the mine at Kirkland Lake.

Fig. 198. Hollinsworth ink recording assembly with the Heiland geophone pickup for use underground at Lake Shore mines.

Fig. 199. Hollinsworth pen and ink recording mechanism in detail. At the left is the recording drum, at the right the ink reservoir. The pen is a stainless steel capillary tube clamped at the ink well and controlled by a light rod attached to the dynamic loud-speaker in place of the phonograph needle.

minute. Experiments down in the mine with another Heiland geophone and a Brush crystal pick-up connected to an amplifier and pen recorder developed by V. Hollinsworth of the Dominion Observatory showed that subaudible snapping noises could be recorded.

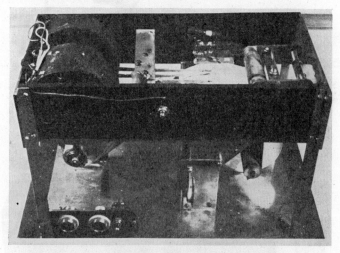

Fig. 200. Modified Obert recorder. The teledeltos paper is drawn from a roller underneath on the left, over a metal platen in the (center) right upper center, down to a roller on the lower right. The three pens of the recording units can be seen over the paper.

Fig. 201. On the left, two complete Obert recording sets operating on the 4200' level in the Lake Shore Mines. On the right is the writer coil, magnet, and stylus of an Obert unit.

With the aid of prospecting seismographs built by the Seismograph Service Corporation of Tulsa, Oklahoma, and a Leet amplifier and recorder all leased from Harvard University, the frequency of the vibrations generated by these snappings and by the larger bursts was found to be between 200 and 400 cycles per second, whereas the frequencies due to blasts and mine traffic were less than 100 cycles per second. Therefore, suitable filtering apparatus was sought to segregate the bursts and snappings.

Meanwhile, since 1938, Doctor Leonard A. Obert[101] and his associates had been struggling with the burst problem in the Lake Superior mining area, particularly in the Calumet and Hecla mine at Ahmeek, Keweenaw County, Michigan, and had developed an amplifier and recorder that were reasonably satisfactory. With Obert's co-operation this design with slight modifications was adopted and built for Lake Shore Mines at Kirkland Lake. The piezoelectric pick-ups for use with the Obert recorders were built by Zack Gibbs in the electronics laboratory at Lake Shore Mines. They were designed for insertion in deep drill-holes and have an outside diameter of only 1¼ inches and an over-all length of eight inches. The piezoelectric element is a two-layered Rochelle Salt crystal two and one-half inches long by three-quarters of an inch wide and one quarter of an inch thick wrapped in silver foil, which serves as one electrode, and separated by a strip of silver foil, which serves as the other electrode. The double crystal is held rigidly at one end like a spring board. When the free end vibrates, the crystal is flexed and the resulting piezoelectric effect causes a slight current to flow through the wire circuit which is connected to the silver foil and includes one coil of a small matching transformer also mounted inside the tube. An insulated two-wire cable connects the other side of the transformer to the Obert amplifier outside the drill-hole which in turn amplifies the current half a million times. The amplified current is led through and rotates the stylus coil suspended between the poles of a permanent magnet in the Obert recorder. The record is made on teledeltos paper by a small electric current which passes continuously from the point of the stylus or writing pen through the paper to a metal platen underneath. The paper needs no processing, so that the record is visible and is ready for immediate use.

It was soon discovered that small subaudible snaps cannot be picked up at distances greater than fifty to seventy-five feet nor

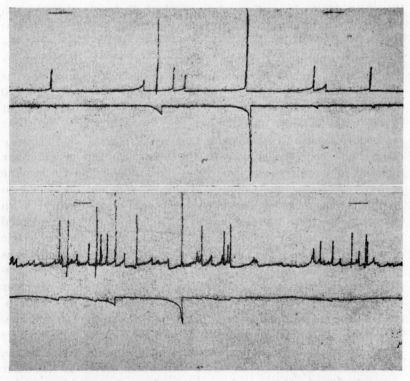

Fig. 202. Records on teledeltos paper obtained with an Obert recorder in Lake Shore Mines. Above, the widely spaced offsets due to subaudible snaps indicate only moderate activity; below, the close spacing indicates acutely active conditions.

Fig. 203. Drift on the 3950' level in Lake Shore Mines damaged in
the rock burst of January 29, 1943.

across a fault or vein. This is a great advantage because it sharply
defines an active zone, but it also makes it necessary to plant the
geophones directly in the suspected mass of ore or rock.

In the latter part of 1942 a locale in the Lake Shore Mines known
as the West Pillar was selected. Geophones were installed in thirty-

Fig. 204. Drift in Lake Shore Mines completely blocked by the
rock burst of January 29, 1943.

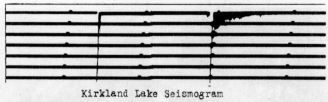

Kirkland Lake Seismogram

Ottawa Seismogram

Rockburst of January 29, 1943

Fig. 205. Violent rock burst of January 29, 1943, recorded by the surface seismograph at Lake Shore Mines and by the Benioff seismograph at Ottawa. Note that the smaller burst in the preceding minute on the Kirkland Lake record also recorded faintly at Ottawa.

foot holes in the hanging wall, which had proved to be more active than the foot wall. They were distributed on the 3825-, 3950-, 4075-, 4200-, and 4325-foot levels. A regular program of recording and counting snaps was begun January 2, 1943. The arrangement was exceedingly fortunate for it proved to be the exact site of a major burst. At 2:10 a.m., January 29, 1943, a burst occurred which affected every level of the West Pillar. Every geophone was lost as well as one recorder. Such was the energy of the burst that it recorded well at Ottawa. Another major burst which wrecked the West Pillar occurred on March 31. It was also recorded at Ottawa.

The results up to the end of August, 1943, are thus summarized by Hodgson.[102] "The sub-audible method, properly applied, definitely indicates the location of pressure zones and permits a study of their shift from one point to another. So far as experience shows to date, ground is unsafe when the average total count per minute is nearly 100. It may not burst, but the risk is great and men should be removed from the area. If it does not burst, the count will soon fall and mining can be resumed until further warning signs appear."

Among the many causes of rock burst phenomena that have been suggested is residual stress or elastic hysteresis, a "yesterday effect" of having been overstrained once upon a time. When a perfectly elastic body is subjected to external forces that change its size or shape, these external forces are resisted by a system of internal forces called elastic stresses. As the external force, or load — often misnamed "stress" — is increased, the strain or change of size and shape increases and the internal stresses increase in proportion.

When the external forces are removed, the elastic stress will restore the body to the size and shape it had before the load was applied; that is it will return to its initial unstrained and unstressed state. This behavior of a perfectly elastic body is described by Hooke's law: *Stress is proportional to strain.*

However, no natural body is *perfectly* elastic. For short periods of time and up to a certain degree of strain called the *elastic limit* many substances closely approximate perfect elasticity. Each rock or mineral has its own elastic limit. Beyond the elastic limit a body is said to be *overstrained.* The internal stress increases with the load but not steadily nor in exact proportion to the strain. Minor failures and internal readjustments such as cracking and snapping occur. The value of the elastic stress or internal resistance at which complete failure occurs is known as the *ultimate strength* of the material.

Even within the elastic limit, but over very long periods of time, comparable with geologic ages, it is believed that molecular readjustment and recrystallization into denser mineral assemblages will reduce elastic stress and strain and adjust buried masses of rock to the deforming load. When the overlying materials are eroded away, or the load is otherwise removed, these rocks will be in unstable equilibrium with the new surroundings. They will develop differential stresses similar to those in unannealed glass which often exceed the ultimate strength of the glass and cause failure by cracking, chipping, or even explosion. This is supposed to be the explanation of many rock bursts, especially those in quarry floors and shallow excavations. Hodgson notes the occurrence at Lake Shore Mines of many large snaps and salvos strong enough to be recorded by the surface seismograph which originate at depths far beyond the deepest workings of any of the mines at Kirkland Lake. Hodgson classifies rock bursts descriptively as *crush bursts* due to failure under compression of large blocks of rock, *spall bursts* due to spalling of the walls of openings under overstrain, and *slip bursts* due to slippage of rock on fault planes either exposed or far in the walls.

Compression and Deformation of Rocks and Minerals

In order to discover the behavior of rocks and minerals under load, some interesting laboratory studies have been made. It is found by L. H. Adams and others that most rock specimens when placed under hydrostatic or all-round pressure yield rather easily at first until a certain pressure is reached, and then resist further compres-

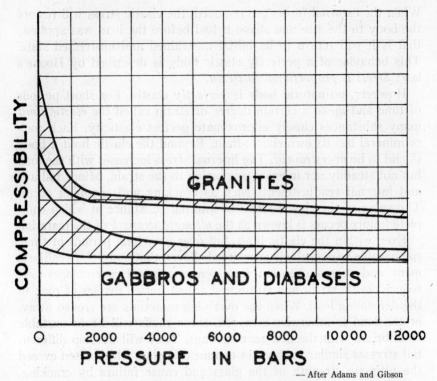

Fig. 206. Compressibility as function of pressure (1 bar = 0.002 lb./sq. ft.). The width of the shaded areas represents the variation within the class.

sion in such a way that the rate of decrease of volume with increasing pressure is small and almost linear. This behavior is supposed to be due to the porosity of most rocks. The first effect of the applied pressure is to close up the empty spaces between the grains. The next effect is to compress the grains themselves.

If, in addition to the confining or hydrostatic pressure there is applied an extra pressure in one direction, the mineral or rock will change its shape. When the deforming force is small so that the strain remains within the elastic limit of the material, the specimen will recover its original shape when the deforming force is removed. But if greater force is applied the rock will yield by plastic flow. F. D. Adams placed a cylinder of rock in a tight-fitting steel jacket and compressed the rock by means of pistons fitting in the jacket. Griggs[103] confined the specimens in kerosene. When the specimen

Fig. 207. Solenhofen limestone broken in longitudinal compression under a confining pressure of about three tons per square inch.

Fig. 208. Solenhofen limestone sheared but not completely ruptured under a confining pressure of six tons to the square inch.

Fig. 209. Solenhofen limestone flaked and deformed plastically but not ruptured under a confining pressure of 125,500 pounds to the square inch.

Fig. 210. Solenhofen limestone plastically deformed 30.3 per cent without failure under a confining pressure of seven and one-half tons per square inch and a differential deforming force of more than six tons to the square inch.

was enclosed in steel it was prevented from fracturing; but when confined in a liquid it would eventually show surface shear lines in large numbers as the force was increased, and would finally fail.

Thus, a block of strong, compact limestone, confined under a pressure four thousand times as great as that of the atmosphere at sea level, was subjected by Griggs to an additional end force. This force was gradually increased until the limestone broke with longitudinal fractures and a shear fractures at about 45° outlining a shear pyramid.

As the confining pressure was increased the longitudinal fracturing decreased and the ultimate strength of the rock increased. Under 10,000 atmospheres confining pressure, which is approximately equivalent to burial under the weight of a twenty-two mile thickness of rock, a cylinder of Solenhofen limestone was plastically deformed and withstood a differential pressure of 185,000 pounds per square inch on its ends without failure. When the differential pressure was removed, the limestone cylinder was observed to grow slowly longer by an amount several hundred per cent greater than would have been expected from the elastic properties of the deformed limestone in the texture of which no change could be detected even under the microscope. This phenomenon of gradual recovery is called *elastic after-working*. It has a bearing on residual stress in the earth's crust which was mentioned as a possible cause of rock bursts.

Bridgman[104] applied shearing couples to powdered rocks and minerals by twisting them under high confining pressures. He found that each substance had its own individual behavior. Most yielded to deformation, not continuously, but by jumps. Some changed their character. Thus graphite ceased to flow and became an abrasive instead of a lubricant when sufficiently sheared. In general, the internal resistance to shear strain increases as the hydrostatic confining pressure on the material is increased. When a constant torque is applied some elements, as for example silver, flow rapidly at first, then slow down and eventually refuse to flow at all. The mineral mica, on the other hand, breaks down and becomes a lubricant under excessive shearing.

Thus gradually and by dint of ingenious but long and difficult experiments does the scientist and the engineer gain further insight into the nature of the materials with which we all must work. Thus by application of the scientific principles and engineering methods of seismology, we solve many problems of our work-a-day world.

Chapter XVI

PROSPECTING WITH SEISMOGRAPHS

Western people are familiar with the hoary figure of the prospector grown gray at his trade, who loads his burro with his grub stake and his kit of mining tools and trudges off into the mountain wilderness to seek elusive ore veins. And many a bonanza does he have to his credit.

After him comes the geologist with a scientific knowledge of mineralization, and discovers fabulous wealth beneath the unsuspecting feet of the old prospector. But there comes a time when the easy prospects have all been located and even the most skilled geologist seeks in vain for more. Then comes the geophysicist and locates the completely invisible.

Petroleum is one of our most important mineral deposits. But, unlike metallic ores, petroleum is mobile. It exists in the pores of rock like water in a sponge; and it is subjected to confining pressures which depend to a great extent on the load above it. These pressures may be enormous. A column of rock two and a half times as dense as water and one square inch in cross section extending down two miles in the earth would weigh more than twenty thousand tons, or about 7500 times the crushing strength of stone.

Under such enormous forces no cavity can remain open and even pores tend to close. All fluids in the pores are therefore under pressure.

Most of the buried rocks were deposited in ancient seas and contain in their pores salt water that was trapped in the process of deposition. Petroleum is much lighter than water. So, when tiny globules of oil are formed, they begin to migrate under their buoyancy through the salt water in the pores until they finally escape to the earth's surface in an oil seep, or are trapped in the pores of a structure with an impervious cap and accumulate there to form an oil field with gas above, oil between, and salt water pressing up from below.

224

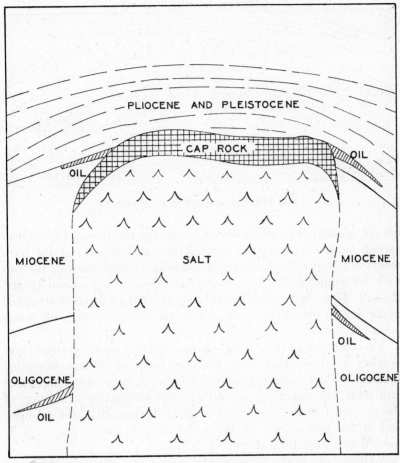

— After Murphy and Judson

Fig. 211. Sketch across the Barber's Hill Salt Dome, Chambers County, Texas.

Oil traps are of many different kinds. One type that has been a prolific producer in the Gulf Coast of Louisiana, Texas, and Mexico, and in Roumania, Germany, and elsewhere is the *salt dome*. A plug of crystalline rock salt sometimes only a few thousand feet wide, as in Sulphur Dome, sometimes miles in diameter as in Boling Dome, has been pushed thousands of feet upward through flat, overlying sediments, like a nail driven into a plank, piercing the lower formations, doming those above. Over the salt is a hard layer

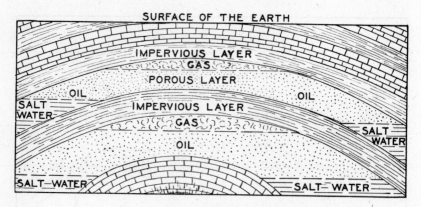

Fig. 212. Oil trapped in an anticline.

mostly of anhydrite which forms a cap for the dome. The hydro-
carbon molecules migrating upward through the pores of the sediments are stopped by some impervious layer sometimes in the cap
rock, sometimes above it, and sometimes come to a dead end against
the salt. Thus they gradually build up gas and oil deposits stratified
according to densities — gas on top, oil in the middle, salt water
below.

A second type of trap is an *anticlinal fold*. If an impervious layer
overlies a porous rock into which globules of oil are migrating
because of their buoyancy, and if these rock layers are compressed
into folds, the migrating oil and gas will accumulate at the top of
the upward fold or anticline. The gas will come first, the oil next,
and at the bottom will be the salt water. A similar trap will be
formed by a structural dome.

A third type is the *stratigraphic trap* of which there are many
variations. An example is the truncated shore line of the East Texas
oil field.

If the layers of ground and of rock were transparent to ordinary
light rays we could see these oil traps beneath our feet. We could
tell by merely looking at them whether the rocks lie flat or are bent
into folds, or are raised in domes, or are cut off by a fault, or pinch
out along an old shore line. We could tell this because the light
waves would penetrate to the rock layers involved and would be
reflected or refracted back up to our eyes.

Now most rocks are opaque to light; but they are transparent
to elastic waves like sound, and if the loudness and frequency of

the sound waves were within the range of audibility we could send down a suitable signal and hear the echoes come up from reflecting surfaces down below. Actually this is impracticable. But a perfectly analogous procedure is feasible and it is known as *seismic prospecting*.

The Signal

To be satisfactory for our purpose the signal must have sufficient energy and it must be quite abrupt. The setting off of a charge of explosive satisfies both requirements. The gases set free by the detonation travel outward with high velocity in all directions and build up in the material, in a very short interval of time, a highly compressed shell. The strain energy thus stored is radiated in the form of elastic waves whose speed depends on both the elasticity and the density. As we have seen in an earlier chapter, the square of the velocity in an ideal, isotropic medium is equal to the elasticity divided by the density in centimeter-gram-second units of measurement.

Now, the earth's crust is made up of layers of different characteristics — sandstones, shales, limestones, igneous rocks — so that there will be abrupt changes of speed as the elastic waves cross their

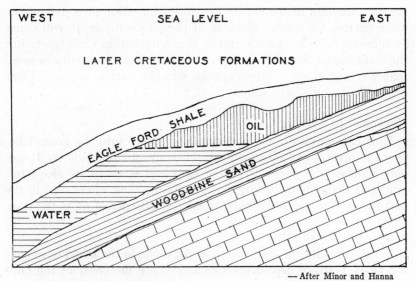

— After Minor and Hanna

Fig. 213. Oil trapped in a truncated shore line. East Texas field.

— Photo by E. A. Hodgson

Fig. 214. Refraction shot in Arkansas.

boundaries. At each such interface there will be, in general, a bend-
ing or refraction of the elastic ray and a reflection of a part of the
wave energy. Of course, increase of pressure with depth will cause
an increase both in density and in elasticity within each layer. But
the resulting increase in velocity per foot of depth is usually so small
that we may think of the rays as straight within any one layer
unless the layer is very thick.

Response to the Signal

How can an elastic wave signal going down into the ground betray the presence of oil in a trap? Directly, it cannot do so. It can
only indicate the presence of the trap and show us its character,
size, and shape, and thereby assist us in deciding where to drill the
best test well to determine the presence or absence of oil in the trap.

Salt Dome Response

Let us consider the response of a salt dome in the midst of unconsolidated Tertiary deposits somewhere along the coast of the Gulf
of Mexico. The speed of longitudinal waves in salt is roughly twice

as great as in the Tertiary deposits — 16,000 ft./sec. as against 8000 ft./sec. Hence, if a longitudinal elastic wave is generated in the sediments and strikes the rock salt, a part of the wave energy will be reflected back as a longitudinal wave and a part will go into the salt and will be separated at once into two waves, the one longitudinal and the other transverse, both of which will be refracted away from the direct path but by different amounts. Thus if the incident ray impinges on the salt boundary along a path which makes an angle of 10° with the normal to the boundary, the re-

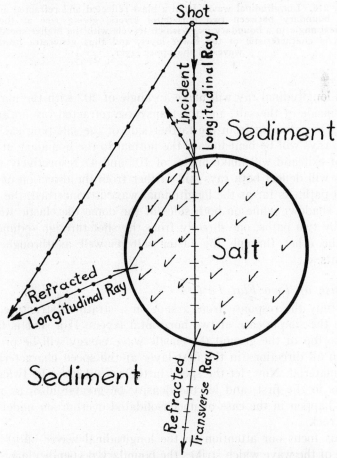

Fig. 215.   Refraction of horizontal rays by a salt plug. Viewed from above.

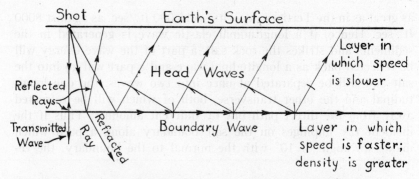

Fig. 216. Longitudinal waves from a blast reflected and refracted at the boundary between two horizontal layers, giving rise at the critical angle to a boundary wave which travels with the higher speed that is characteristic of the lower layer, and thus generates head waves in the upper layer.

fracted longitudinal ray will make an angle of 20° with the normal on the inside of the salt, and the transverse refracted ray an angle of 11°. On emerging from the farther side of the salt plug each of the two rays will be bent toward the normal to the boundary at the point of exit and will make angles of 10° and 4° respectively with it. This will deflect both rays still farther from the direction of the original path. As far as the longitudinal wave is concerned, the salt casts a shadow; while on both sides of the dome the elastic waves arrive by two paths, one directly from the shot through sediments only, the other through the faster salt as well as through the sediments.

Response of Two Flat Layers

To study the response from a shot on a stratified structure, let us take the simple case of two horizontal layers. If a shot is fired near the top of the ground the elastic wave energy will be propagated in all directions in the first layer at the speed characteristic of the material. Now, let the speed in the second layer be twice as great as in the first, and let the density be greater also, as may readily happen in the case of unconsolidated overburden underlain by bed rock.

Let us focus our attention on the longitudinal waves only. The portion of the wave which strikes the boundary perpendicularly will penetrate into the second layer without deviation, although a small portion of the energy will be reflected back into the upper layer because of the change in density. As the angle of incidence, that is, the angle between the ray and the normal, increases as more of the wave front hits the boundary, more energy will be reflected and the transmitted rays will be bent more and more away from the normal. At last a critical value of the angle of incidence will be reached at which the refracted rays will be directed along the under side of the boundary and will generate a *boundary wave*.

Now, whenever anything moves through a medium at greater speed than is characteristic of wave motion in that particular

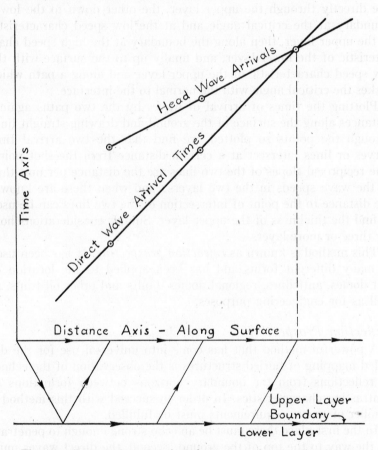

Fig. 217. Intersection of arrival-time curves for the direct wave and the head wave.

medium, as, for example, when a ship travels faster than water waves, or a projectile flies faster than sound in air, *bow waves* or *head waves* are generated. Therefore the boundary wave travelling along the interface with the higher speed that is characteristic of the lower layer may be expected to generate in the upper layer a series of head waves which, once generated, will leave the interface at the critical angle and will travel through the upper layer at the slower speed characteristic of that layer until they reach the top and are observed.

Hence, beyond a certain critical distance, there will be two paths by which the wave signals will arrive at points on the surface, the one directly through the upper layer, the other down to the lower boundary at the critical angle and at the low speed characteristic of the upper layer, then along the boundary at the high speed characteristic of the lower layer, and finally up to the surface with the low speed characteristic of the upper layer and along a path which makes the critical angle with the normal to the interface.

Plotting the times of arrival of waves by the two paths against distances along the surface of the ground and drawing straight lines through the points so plotted, we find that the two arrival time curves or lines intersect at a certain distance from the shot point. The reciprocal slopes of the two lines are the distance per unit time or the wave speeds in the two layers; and when these are known, the distance to the point of intersection of the two lines can be used to find the thickness of the upper layer. Similar considerations hold for three or more layers.

This method is known as *refraction prospecting*. It has been used in many different forms and has been applied to the location of salt domes, anticlines, regional domes, faults and other oil traps, as well as for engineering purposes.

Reflection Prospecting

A powerful method that has come into universal use for the detailed mapping of buried structures is the observation of the echoes or reflections from the boundary horizons between formations of contrasting characteristics. In order to succeed with this method a number of severe requirements must be fulfilled.

In the first place there must be an echo strong enough to penetrate all the way to the top of the ground. Second, the direct waves must be shielded off so that they will not drown out the echo. Third, the

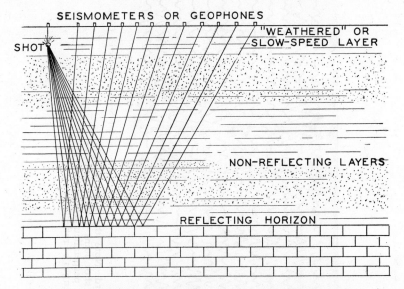

Fig. 218. Schematic representation of rays from the shot point to the seismometers in reflection prospecting.

receiving and recording apparatus must be so designed that the echo may be positively identified as such. Fourth, the interval between the departure of the signal and the return of the echo must be timed with an accuracy approaching one millisecond, that is, one one-thousandth of a second.

Only the great advances of modern electronics and radio communications engineering could have made possible the highly efficient seismic prospecting apparatus that is meeting so successfully the exacting requirements of the reflection method.

Producing the Echo

At the top of the ground there is a layer within which the speed of elastic waves is relatively slow and the rate of absorption or damping is high. This is often called the *weathered layer,* although it seems to have no obvious connection with geological or chemical weathering and it is not a distinct geological stratum. Its thickness, which may be quite variable, and the velocity characteristic of it are usually determined by a refraction shot.

Whatever the nature of the slow-speed layer, it acts as an effective block to the transmission of a satisfactory signal, so that it is neces-

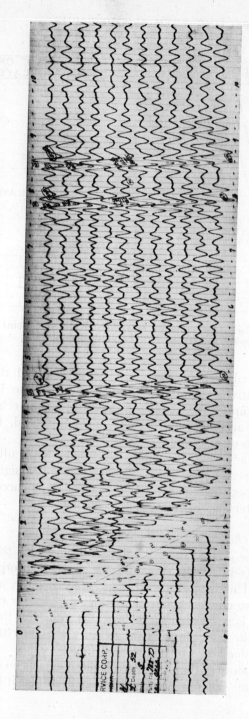

Fig. 219. Twelve-channel reflection record. Note the slope of first arrivals with increasing distance from the shot point to the successive geophones, while the echoes run almost perpendicularly across because of the small differences in the length of reflected paths.

— Courtesy Seismograph Service Corp.

— Courtesy Seismograph Service Corp.

Fig. 221. A drilling truck.

sary to set off the charge beneath it. Since the thickness of the layer often exceeds 75 feet, a power drill with the usual assortment of bits and other paraphernalia of well drilling must be used. Drilling mud and even removable casing may be required to prevent caving. In wet areas, such as swamps, sufficient water is at hand to supply the drill; but a tender truck with a water tank usually accompanies the drill truck.

The blasting caps and dynamite are carried in a special blaster's truck equipped with a blasting machine or relay.

Recognition of Echoes

So much of the energy of the signal goes by other paths that the echo which arrives at a given point on the earth's surface is very weak in comparison with the waves that are still coming directly from the source. How can we recognize the echo? With the single mechanical-optical seismographs that were used for prospecting in the early twenties this was a well-nigh insoluble problem.

— Photo by E. A. Hodgson

Fig. 222. Loading the charge into the shot hole.
Note the shot point geophone beside the hole.

Reflection Seismographs

In order to appreciate the scientific and engineering triumphs that were involved in the development of the modern reflection seismograph, let us look at some of the apparently contradictory requirements that were set by the echo to be observed. The energy contained in the echo is so small that it must be magnified millions of times to be easily observable. On the other hand the seismometers used to pick up the echo must not be so sensitive as to be affected by small extraneous disturbances in their immediate neighborhood, such as the waving of grass in a breeze. The seismometers must be portable yet so rugged that they will not be damaged by riding over rough roads and so stable that incidental jars will not affect their performance. The detectors must be spread out on a line hundreds of feet long, running away from the shot point in order to indicate the wave front of the arriving echo; but they must all record together on a single timing system in order to indicate to a millisecond the length of time the signal was on the way. The line of detectors must be relatively near the shot point so that the direct waves will have passed before the echo arrives. But the direct waves are so large in comparison with the echo that even the aftermath of their passage would mask the echoes unless shunted out in some way.

How did the geophysical engineers meet this multiple challenge? In the first place they chose to use electrical systems so that the

— Photo by E. A. Hodgson

Fig. 223. Blaster, third from left, beside the blasting truck, has just pushed down the plunger of the blasting machine, thus firing the shot.

detecting end could be placed at a distance from the recording end and the connection made by cable. The detecting element was, of course, a seismometer based on the principles already described in the previous chapters on seismographs. But its design could be very simple; because its short free period and comparatively low sensitivity permitted close coupling of the pendulum to the frame. The electromechanical transducer adopted was more often either of the moving coil or of the moving magnet variety; less often of the variable resistance or variable capacity type. This produced a small rugged unit that could be handled rather roughly in the field without danger of damage or alteration of adjustment.

The required magnification of

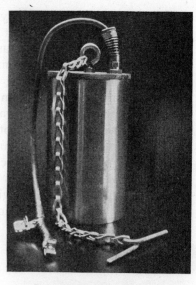

— Courtesy Seismograph Service Corp.

Fig. 224. A seismometer or geophone. Note the carrying chain and the wire with two connections for attachment to the cable which leads to the recording truck.

several million times is attained by means of an electronic amplifier. This amplifier is so designed as to serve at the same time as a band filter, to let through only the desired range of frequencies — thirty to sixty per second — which are characteristic of the echoes, and to shut out high frequency noises and low frequency ground roll.

The entire set of amplifiers, one for each seismometer, is built into a compact unit, which also contains the control panel for the entire system, an automatic volume control, and a delayer which throttles all the amplifiers and prevents them from gaining their full effectiveness until the waves coming direct from the shot will have had time to pass by. The automatic volume control then takes over and adjusts all the amplifiers so that each succeeding echo elicits an optimum response and makes a legible record.

The recording camera is a triumph of compactness that owes some of its features to the needs of the first World War. There are three main parts to such a camera: the galvanometers, the timing system, and the photographic recording system. One of the solutions to the problem of causing a whole bank of galvanometers to record together on a film or strip of photographic paper no wider than the hand was to use the Einthoven type and to stretch the strings, whose shadow is photographed, side by side on a species of harp between the poles of a broad horseshoe magnet. Another solution, much more in use today, was the development of a moving coil galvanometer of the D'Arsonval type smaller than a lead pencil, so that a dozen or more could be mounted side by side in the space of a very few inches. Beams of light from convenient sources are reflected from mirrors on the moving coils to a cylindrical lens and each is focused as a brilliant spot of light on the surface of the recording sheet.

— Courtesy Seismograph Service Corp.

Fig. 225. Set of six amplifiers below. Control panel in upper right. Delayer in upper left.

A timing system often used consists of an oscillatory circuit resonating with a 50 cycle or 100 cycle precision tuning fork and driving an oscillograph in synchronism with it. A beam of light reflected from the tiny mirror of the oscillograph is thrown across the length of the cylindrical lens at each to-and-fro movement of the oscillograph coil, thus producing sharp timing lines on the record every ten or every five milliseconds.

— Courtesy Seismograph Service Corp.

Fig. 226. Seismic reflection camera resting on the top of its case.

— Courtesy Seismograph Service Corp.

Fig. 227. A recording truck.

The record is made by pulling a strip of sensitive bromide paper past the cylindrical lens at a chosen speed of two to three feet per second. A roll of some 200 feet of the paper is placed in the magazine of the camera. As the paper is exposed it is automatically drawn into a second chamber from which it can be removed for processing.

The amplifiers and the camera are usually mounted in a light-tight recording truck together with photographic developing and fixing equipment, telephone for communication with the blasting truck, wire reels for the various cables, and racks to hold the seismometers when in transit.

Chapter XVII

MICROSEISMS AND STORMS AT SEA

It is a fascinating fact but difficult to realize that all day long and through the night we are riding waves in the solid earth. The waves to which we now refer have no connection with earthquakes or with any of the other phenomena of which we have been speaking in the previous chapters. These waves are so small that as we ride them we rise and fall only a few millionths of an inch; yet they tell a fascinating story.

Some of the waves are long and some are short. The short waves are scarcely more than a mile from crest to crest or trough to trough. These have been known to scientists for only a few years. The next longer type of these waves is the most interesting. They were discovered and studied for the first time by a Barnabite monk, Timoteo Bertelli, in Florence, Italy. He called them "microseisms." If we were able to see the waves with our unaided eye, we would find that the time which elapses between the passage of one wave crest and the passage of the next is anywhere from 3 to 7 seconds, and that the crests are several miles apart. These waves are usually larger in winter than they are in summer, and their appearance changes from day to day.

However, in summer and in winter there are times when the waves increase in size to many times their normal height; and they will continue large for many hours or even for two or three days. Ever since the time of Bertelli, back in the sixties and seventies of the nineteenth century, people have wondered about these waves. Scientists studied them and advanced many theories to account for them, but none of these theories were proved. There seemed to be some connection between the size of the waves and the weather at a distance. Some scientists advanced the opinion that they were produced by the beating of storm waves of the sea against rocky coasts. Others thought they saw a direct connection between these

242

waves and storms over the ocean, including hurricanes and typhoons. For years national and international committees of seismologists studied the seismographic records of these waves and reported the results. Statisticians compared the data with conditions existing on the weather maps. But no theory was definitely proved until a direct method of attack on the problem was devised by Reverend J. E. Ramirez, S.J., under the direction of the author at St. Louis University. The plan consisted in the designing of seismographs especially for the study of these microseisms and their installation at

Fig. 227a. Reverend J. E. Ramirez, S.J.

the corners of a right-angled triangle. Two pairs of seismographs were set up, one pair about four miles apart to record motion in an east and west direction, the other pair also about four miles apart to record motion in a north and south direction. Two seismographs were placed at the vertex of the right triangle thus formed and two at the ends of the legs. When a wave front traveled across this triangle, it arrived first at one, then at another of these seismographs. In order to time their arrival, leased wires carried identical time signals to all four of the seismographs every few seconds. Such a

Fig. 227b. Macelwane-Sprengnether seismograph for microseisms used by Father Ramirez.

triangular arrangement of seismograph emplacements is called a *tripartite station.*

The time intervals observed between successive arrivals at the three component stations of the tripartite arrangement obviously permitted the measurement of the speed at which the waves were traveling and the direction from which they came. It was found that at St. Louis the average speed of travel of the microseismic waves was about 1.6 miles per second. But what was most interesting about this type of microseism was that in every case when the waves rose up to unusual heights, rising and falling more or less rhythmically in groups, they were coming from a storm at sea such as a hurricane or an extratropical storm of great intensity. At the same time that Ramirez was engaged in his investigations at St. Louis University, Trommsdorff at the University of Göttingen was carrying on similar research with portable seismographs arranged in a triangle and was arriving at similar conclusions.

At the beginning of World War II it was necessary to stop all radio communications between ships at sea and radio stations on land. This lack of communication crippled the weather forecasts and exposed naval vessels, convoys, and airplanes to danger of

shipwreck by sailing into the track of a hurricane whose existence
was unknown. In order, in some measure, to ward off this danger,
both the army and navy sent out airplanes at frequent intervals to
reconnoiter; but this reconnaissance was hazardous to men and
planes alike. It was uncertain, besides, because it was limited mostly
to daylight hours; and, in the vast expanse of the ocean, storms
were readily overlooked. Even in the case of those that were discovered, the location and direction of movement were difficult to
determine by one observation. Therefore, the joint Meteorological
Committee of the Chiefs of Staff of the Army, Navy, and Weather
Bureau cast about for other methods of forecasting and were attracted by the possibilities of microseisms and especially by the

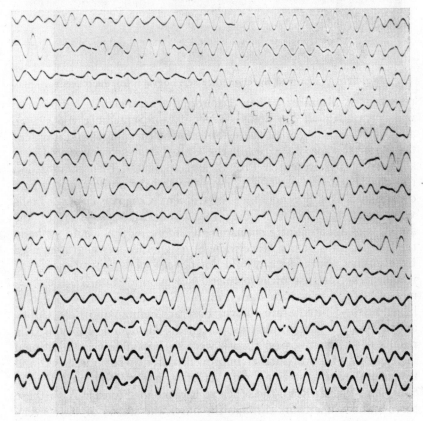

Fig. 227c. Storm microseisms recorded with the Macelwane-
Sprengnether seismograph.

Fig. 227d. Improved Sprengnether seismograph for microseisms.

research of Ramirez. They accordingly arranged a conference, which was held at St. Louis University on September 8–9, 1943, and which recommended the establishment of tripartite stations of the Ramirez type. As a result, the United States Navy established a Microseismic Research Project and appointed Lieutenant Commander M. H. Gilmore officer-in-charge and the author as technical consultant. The Sprengnether Instrument Company of St. Louis was engaged to build seismographs, under the direction of the author and Lieutenant Commander Gilmore, which would embody the best features of the Macelwane-Sprengnether seismographs used by Ramirez, but which would introduce such improvements as would make for ease of adjustment and manipulation. In the summer of 1944, a tripartite station on the Ramirez pattern was established at the United States Naval Base at Guantanamo Bay, Cuba; and a single seismograph was placed at Richmond, Florida. The results of the first season's work were so favorable that additional instruments of a still further improved pattern were purchased and two new tripartite stations were set up — one at Roosevelt Roads, San Juan, Puerto Rico, the other at Richmond, Florida. With these three stations operating through the hurricane season of 1945 every doubt was removed as to the reliability of the method. It was found that all hurricanes and intense extratropical storms set up microseisms of the type under discussion and that the bearing of each storm center could be measured with accuracy from each station as soon as the storm center came within range. This range varied from some 300 miles for small storms to more than 2000 miles for storms of great intensity. Cross bearings from two or more stations located the storm center with a higher degree of accuracy than is possible by any other method. Not only did the bearings point to a storm center over the ocean rather than to a coast subjected to surf, but the microseisms generated by a sudden development of a storm were recorded much too soon to allow the storm waves to travel over the sea to a coast where surf would be produced. The evidence was so conclusive as to convince even the most skeptical adherents of other theories concerning the origin of microseisms. In the tripartite station of the Ramirez type, marine meteorology has a powerful tool for locating and tracking hurricanes, typhoons, and extratropical storms, from the time they are formed until they are dissipated or pass inland.

— Photo by Trefts

Fig. 227e. Sprengnether triple recorder.

There are other vibrations recorded by seismographs which are caused by industrial installations; railway, highway, and city traffic; freezing and thawing of the ground; cooling under radiation; the friction of high winds on a landscape; breakers on the shore, and other phenomena. But these vibrations are of different character from the microseisms produced by storms at sea and may be readily distinguished from them.

APPENDIX A

OUR CHANGING EARTH

In the foregoing chapters it has become increasingly clear to the reader that our so-called *terra firma* is not as stable as most of us would like to think. In fact, taken in the by and large, the surface of our planet is decidedly mobile. Not only is this true of actual earthquakes and other movements at the present time, but geological history teaches us that it has always been so in the past. Hence it will help us to understand earthquakes better if we devote a few pages to an elementary study of the geological forces that are constantly at work on the earth, tearing down, building up, molding the skin of our globe so to speak, folding, distorting, fracturing the rocks of which it is made.

If we descend to the bottom of the Grand Canyon of the Colorado we shall find there a stream which is using its load of sand and gravel to saw a great gash in the earth's crust (Fig. 228). In the walls of that chasm we may read some of the earliest pages of geological history. The dark rocks in the immediate foreground on both sides of the gorge are believed to be among the oldest in the world. They are classed as *Archean,* that is, belonging to the beginning of things geological, from the Greek ἀρχή (arche) the beginning. They have undergone profound changes and have recrystallized under the influence of pressure and heat while deeply buried in the earth so that they are now called *metamorphic rocks* from the Greek μεταμορφικός (changed in form, from μορφή *morphe* — form). Certain flat crystals like mica have arranged themselves along more or less parallel planes so that the rock splits or cleaves readily there. Hence these rocks are called *schists* from the Greek word σχίζω (schizo), I split, divide, and its passive participle σχιστός (schistos) split or cleaved. This inner chasm of the Grand Canyon is popularly known as the Granite Gorge because the walls in places are composed of an *igneous* rock resembling granite which, far back in Archean time,

— Photo by Macelwane

Fig. 228. The Colorado River flowing through the Inner Gorge of the Grand Canyon. Looking upstream near the foot of Bright Angel Trail. Archean Vishnu schists in the foreground.

intruded itself while molten into the schist and then cooled slowly enough to crystallize as it cooled.

Glancing again at Figure 228 we can see in the middle ground on top of the schists a totally different kind of rock. It consists of nearly flat-lying beds or layers, or, as geologists call them, *strata*. An examination of these stratified rocks at close range would show that they are limestones, shales, sandstones, and conglomerates and that the top surfaces of many of the beds carry ripple marks and others show sun cracks. Such stratified rocks are called *sedimentary* because they were formed by cementing and hardening of sediments like the sands and muds of our river bottoms and the sea shore. This Grand Canyon series of sedimentary rocks, while very much younger than the underlying Archean schists and separated from them by an old, old land surface, are nevertheless so immensely old that they stand near the beginnings of life on the earth.

Now if we follow the Bright Angel Trail as it ascends a side canyon away from the river and look back (Fig. 229) we shall recognize these same old sedimentary rocks on top of the schists on the farther side of the Grand Canyon but we shall see that they tilt or dip slightly downward toward the left and seem to form a wedge between the schists below and a precipitous cliff above. The rock in the cliff is a sandstone of a later age and was laid down across the beveled edges of the old sedimentaries. About half way up the right slope of the side canyon in Figure 229 and directly in line with the old sedimentaries across the Grand Canyon we see a small portion of these same old sedimentaries bent around upward into a right angle fold. The other rocks in the foreground on both sides of the picture are a continuation of the Archean schists that occupied the foreground in Figure 228.

Above the cliff of sandstone in Figure 229 the walls of the Grand Canyon widen out, leaving a broad floor between themselves and the Granite Gorge. This broad expanse is called the Tonto platform. It is almost entirely composed of rock of a single age, the Cambrian Tapeats sandstone and the Bright Angel shale (Fig. 230). Geologists

— Photo by Macelwane

Fig. 229. Looking across the Inner Gorge of the Grand Canyon of the Colorado from the Side Canyon through which the Bright Angel Trail descends to the river. A small fold of the Algonkian Grand Canyon System of rocks will be seen on the nearer side of the Gorge in line with a wedge of nearly flat layers of the same system on the farther side. The rocks in the foreground are the Archean Vishnu schists. Those above on the far side of the Inner Gorge are Cambrian sandstones. Three eras are, therefore, represented by the rocks in this picture. They are separated by unconformities indicating great lapse of time between.

— Photo by Macelwane

Fig. 230. Bright Angel shale on the Tonto platform, Grand
Canyon of the Colorado.

have found it convenient, especially for purposes of correlation and
mapping and to avoid the necessity of repeating long descriptions,
to divide the rocks of the Grand Canyon and indeed the rocks of the
whole world into *formations*. Thus the Bright Angel shale is a
formation, a unit in the geological column; one of the succession of
formations that are exposed in the walls of the Grand Canyon between the river and the rim. The division into formations is to a
certain extent arbitrary. The basis for the division is a threefold
one. First, the rocks assigned to one formation may form an obvious
lithological unit that is all of one type, as for example a limestone
of a certain appearance, texture, and composition, wherever it is
found. Second, while the rocks may not be of one homogeneous
type, but may consist, for example, of alternating shales and sandstones, yet the ensemble contrasts strongly with the formations
above and below. Third, the formation may be delimited above
and below by changes in the assemblage of animals and plants that
existed when it was deposited and whose remains are buried in it
as fossils (see Fig. 244), thus giving it a characteristic fossil *fauna*
and *flora* by which it may be recognized although there may be little
or no lithological difference between it and the formations above
and below.

It is customary to name formations after a geographical locality where they are typically exposed. Thus the Archean schists are named *Vishnu schists* after the mountain in the Canyon wall which is called Vishnu's Temple. The *Bright Angel Shale* is named from Bright Angel Canyon in the walls of which the shale is well exposed.

The sediments laid down to form the rocks which are exposed in the walls of the Grand Canyon from the Tonto platform upward to the rim and even beyond on the great plateaus are essentially undisturbed. They accumulated as they lie. Hence the younger formations naturally overlie the older in regular succession. Where this undisturbed condition can be demonstrated as in this case, the order of superposition will determine the temporal sequence of the living forms whose remains are buried in each formation, and this temporal sequence can be used in turn in an obviously disturbed area to discover the order of deposition or "age" of the formations and thus decipher the geologic structure.

To this end geologists throughout the world have correlated their observations and built up a time table. All geological time has been divided into five parts called *eras* whose names are based on their relation to life on the earth. Thus the very earliest era, which is characterized by complete absence of determinable fossils though there are thought to be indications of life, is called the *Archeozoic* era, a Greek word ἀρχαιοζωικός from ἀρχή (*arche*) beginning and ζῷον (zoön) animal.

Since the sedimentary rocks throughout this immense sequence of formations are similar in composition and texture to those which were formed but yesterday and are forming from sediments today, the geologist postulates that the same agencies were responsible for them all.

Some of these *geological agencies* are *weathering, running water, the sea, ice, plants* and *animals, igneous activity,* and, finally, *deforming forces* within the earth.

Weathering is the gradual decay and disintegration of rocks under the influence of rain, frost, chemical action, and other subaerial influences. Some rock types weather faster than others. Even in the same formation different degrees of hardness and kinds of cement between grains may cause wide variations in the rate of weathering (Fig. 231). The Grand Canyon is a typical example of the work of *running water* on a large scale. But the erosive action of running water begins much farther back in the tiny rills that carry the

TABLE I. GEOLOGICAL TIME TABLE

Eras	Periods	Epochs	Characteristic Animal Life	Mountain Building Events
Caenozoic	Quaternary	Recent	Age of Man	California Coast Ranges
		Pleistocene (Great Ice Age)		Apennines
				Rocky Mountain Uplifts
				Cascades
	Tertiary	Pliocene		
		Miocene		Himalayas
		Oligocene	Age of Mammals	Alps
		Eocene		
		Paleocene		
Mesozoic	Cretaceous			Andes
	Jurassic		Age of Reptiles	Rocky Mountains
	Triassic			Sierra Nevada
	Carboniferous	Permian		
		Pennsylvanian	Age of Amphibians	Appalachians
		Mississippian		
	Devonian			
	Silurian		Age of Fishes	Scottish Highlands
	Ordovician			
	Cambrian	Upper Cambrian		
		Middle Cambrian	Age of Invertebrates	
		Lower Cambrian		
Proterozoic	Algonkian			
Archeozoic	Archean			Laurentians

Fig. 231. Differential weathering in the fountain formation of carboniferous age, Mushroom Park, near Manitou, Colorado.

run-off of a rainstorm. Where there is little or no cover of vegetation to hold back the run-off these little rills, coalescing like the branches of a tree into trunk streams, cut a system of gullies in the soil of every slope and eventually produce a badland topography (Fig.

Fig. 232. Gully erosion in Nelson Canyon along the San Andreas Rift.

— Photo by Rev. V. C. Stechschulte, S.J.

Fig. 233. The Royal Gorge of the Arkansas River, west of Canon City, Colorado. View from the plateau looking in a southwesterly direction toward Webster Park. The shadow cast by the suspension bridge at noon may be seen as black line across the river more than 1000 feet below.

232). If a drainage channel has been eroded below the water table, that is, the level at which all the pores of the rocks are permanently

— Photo by Rev. V. C. Stechschulte, S.J.

Fig. 233a. The raging torrent of the Arkansas River tearing through the Royal Gorge.

Fig. 234. Large expanse of mud and sand in the channel of the
Missouri River west of Washington, Missouri, awaiting the next
flood to move it onward toward the sea.

filled with water, then there will be a flow of water into this channel
from the sides and we shall have a brook, a creek, or a river, depending on the size of the valley and on the quantity of water normally
flowing in it. Pure water is a poor cutting agent. Thus the Niagara
River above the falls carries only clear water from Lake Erie and
can erode its bed but little. Cutting tools are needed in the form of
suspended sand and pebbles and of boulders rolled along the bottom.

Fig. 235. Cross-bedded Cambrian sandstone in the recent gorge
cut by the Wisconsin River to form the Dells.

— Photo by Macelwane

Fig. 236. Sand bars on the Wisconsin River near Prairie
du Chien, Wisconsin.

The Arkansas River with a sufficient gradient to give it a high
velocity has been able in very recent geological time to cut the Royal
Gorge one fifth of a mile deep through a plateau of granite (Figs.
233 and 233a).

Where the slope is more gentle rivers move their loads of mud
and sand and gravel only gradually, much of the sediment finding
a temporary resting place in the flood plain (Fig. 234) between
freshets and awaiting the next great flood to move onward in its
journey toward the sea which will be its last resting place. Thus
sediments are worked over and over. The Wisconsin River, for
example, cuts through the cross-bedded Cambrian sandstone that is
so conspicuous in the Dells (Fig. 235) and farther down its course
also flows through the St. Peter sandstone of Ordovician age. The
sand derived from both these sources is carried downstream toward
the Mississippi River step by step, now rolling along with the current, now deposited in sandbars long enough for shrubbery and
forest trees to grow upon them (Fig. 236).

The sea is not only a final depository of land sediments but is an
active eroding agent where headlands are exposed to the waves. The
violently agitated sea water picks up sand, pebbles, and even large
boulders and hurls them against the cliff, thus undermining it and at
the same time exerting explosive pressure by the compression of the
air in the cavities. The waves thus cut a characteristic cliff and rock

Fig. 237. Abalone Point on the Southern California coast at low tide, showing the wave-cut cliff and rock bench.

Fig. 238. Storm waves breaking on the shore of the Pacific Ocean just outside the Golden Gate, San Francisco, California. Mile light and the Marin Peninsula in the distance.

Fig. 239. Sand beach and dunes on the Pacific shore near San
Francisco, California.

Fig. 240. The Asulkan Glacier in the Selkirk Mountains of British
Columbia. Note the crevasses in the surface of the ice, the medial
moraine in the left middle ground, and the well-developed terminal
moraine on the right.

bench (Fig. 237). The material broken loose is pounded by the surf (Fig. 238) and carried by currents along shore until it comes temporarily to rest as sand on a beach, whence the wind may drive it inland to form dunes (Fig. 239) or it may be buried under further deposits by the sea advancing over the land.

An impressive geologic agent is *ice* in the form of a moving glacier. Valley glaciers form whenever the snow falls faster on the higher slopes of mountains than it can melt in the course of a year. The hardening snow called the *neve* in the catch basin is gradually pushed out under its own weight plucking away and pulling along with it such blocks of rock as are frozen to it around the rim and on the bottom. These fragments grasped in the ice along the bottom and sides of the glacier form very efficient planing tools, polishing, scratching, and grooving the rock floor over which they ride and becoming in turn faceted and striated themselves. Where the ice is melting along the sides and at the terminus the debris is dropped in a heap called a moraine (Fig. 240). The whole continent of Greenland is covered with an outward moving field of ice. Many times during geological history large parts of other continents were thus covered by continental glaciers; but the Pleistocene epoch of the Quaternary period is especially known as the Great Ice Age. No

Fig. 241. Large glacial grooves in limestone on Kelley's Island in Lake Erie.

Fig. 242. Petrified log in Triassic shale and sandstone north of Adamana, Arizona. The tree belonged to an extinct species of Araucaria, or conifer related to the Norfolk Island pine.

less than four times were Canada and the northern United States invaded by ice during that time, leaving their footprints, as it were, in the form of innumerable lakes and swamps, moraines, boulder

Fig. 243. Plant growth encroaching on an arm of glacial Lake Beulah, near Mukwonago, Wisconsin, and gradually transforming it into a swampy meadow.

clays, wind blown dust called *loess* (from the German *löss*), and frequently scratches and deep grooves in the underlying bed rock, telling us the direction in which the ice was moving (Fig. 241).

Important as are all of these nonliving agents in the gradual building up of the sedimentary rocks of the earth's crust, and adding to these the chemical precipitation of sediments by sea water, we shall find that living beings have played a no less striking part. Coal is wholly composed of the carbonized tissue of plants. Sometimes tissue is replaced by silica, thus giving us petrified forests (Fig. 242). Algae live in enormous numbers in nearly all the waters of the globe. Plant growth encroaches upon ponds and lakes and eventually transforms them into meadows (Fig. 243). Animals live and die in great profusion in the sea, especially on the continental shelves, and whole formations are often built up by their remains accumulating on the shallow sea bottom (Fig. 244).

Water-laid sediments are stratified; ice-laid sediments are not. Both types of formation, however, are deposited under the influence of the force of gravity, and hence *tend always to assume a horizontal attitude*. How then are we to explain the highly *tilted* strata we find exposed at so many places on the earth's surface? Evidently other forces besides those we have been considering have been at work.

— Photo by Macelwane

Fig. 244. Scarcely fossilized shells of mollusks in Purisima sandstone of Pliocene age, north shore of Monterey Bay, California.

Fig. 245. Slightly overturned strata of arkosic sandstone belonging to the Fountain formation of Pennsylvanian age, Garden of the Gods, Colorado Springs, Colorado.

Marine formations which must originally have been horizontal are found tilted away from a mountain front. Differential erosion causes the more resistant strata to stand out boldly in a succession of ridges while valleys and depressions are formed in the softer layers be-

Fig. 246. Cambrian Sawatch sandstone deposited on the irregularly eroded surface of Archean Pike's Peak granite, in Williams Canyon, near Manitou, Colorado.

— Photo by Macelwane

Fig. 247. A monocline in the Huron shale east of Vermilion, Ohio.

tween. In some places the formations have been tilted past the vertical as in the Garden of the Gods (Fig. 245).

The causes of these changes of attitude in the sedimentary rocks must be sought in the forces which are responsible for mountain building and for the elevation of the continents. Underneath the entire succession of sedimentary formations we find rocks of a totally different character which we call *igneous rocks* because they have cooled down to their present condition from the molten state.

But nowhere on the earth do we find evidence of a primordial igneous crust. The igneous rocks we know were either intruded while molten into other rocks or were extruded on top of them. The granites we see have been exposed by erosion after long burial. Many granites were so exposed when the lowermost sedimentary rocks were deposited on their eroded surfaces (Fig. 246). Such a contact is called an unconformity. It indicates a lapse of time sufficient for the underlying rock to be raised up, subjected to subaerial erosion and depressed again beneath the sea to receive the marine sediments that now rest upon it. These changes of level belong to a process of raising and lowering of the land or of sea level which the geologists call *diastrophism*. It plays an important part in the making of continents and in mountain building.

Fig. 248. Intricately folded radiolarian chert of the
Jurassic Franciscan series in Golden Gate Park,
San Francisco, California.

In addition, there are enormous forces at work in the process of
mountain building which fold up rocks and fracture them and push
them over each other. A simple flexure is called a *monocline* (Fig.
247). An upward fold is called an *anticline,* a downward fold a
syncline. Sometimes the pressure is such as to produce intricate
plications (Fig. 248). Erosion may remove the roof of an anticline

— Photo by W. J. Jelinek

Fig. 249. Unconformities in the San
Juan Mountains just south of Ouray,
Colorado, looking southward. Below
are vertical strata of Uncompahgre
quartzite of Algonkian age. Laid
down across their beveled edges are
the Elbert sandstone and Ouray limestone both of Devonian age, dipping
forward toward the north. Above are
the Molas and Hermosa formations
of Pennsylvanian age.

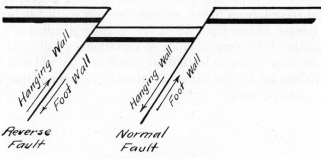

Fig. 250. Types of faults.

— Photo by Rev. J. B. Macelwane, S.J.

Fig. 251. A recent reverse fault near Santa Barbara, California. The uncemented dune sands of Recent age on the left are undisturbed, while the firm shales of Miocene age on the right have been bent around into a drag fold.

and later sediments may be deposited horizontally over the truncated ends of the older beds, thus giving rise to an *angular unconformity* (Fig. 249). Again, the formations may be overstrained in the process of folding and may snap in two. *Faulting* (Figs. 250, 251) is of common occurrence and, as we have seen, it is ordinarily associated with earthquakes. Thus from the beginning of the geological record down to the present time our earth has been subject to changes within and without whose understanding is a necessary condition for a fruitful study of earthquakes and their causes. The reader who wishes to learn more about geology will find in *This Earth of Ours* by Doctor Victor T. Allen[105] an account that is both accurate and fascinating.

APPENDIX B

REFERENCES AND NOTES

(Numbers correspond to small numbers in text)

1. Lawson, Andrew C., *et al.*, "The California Earthquake of April 18, 1906," Report of the Earthquake Investigation Commission, Carnegie Institution of Washington, *Publications*, No. 87, 2 vols. and atlas, 1908–10.
2. Hobbs, W. H., and Johnson, W. D., "The Earthquake of 1872 in the Owens Valley, California," *Gerlands Beiträge zur Geophysik*, Band 10, Originalarbeiten, pp. 352–385, Pl. X–XXIII.
3. Whitney, J. D., "The Owens Valley Earthquake," *Overland Monthly*, Vol. 9, Nos. 2, 3, Aug., Sept., 1872, pp. 120–140, 266–278.
4. Gilbert, G. K., "Lake Bonneville," United States Geological Survey, *Monographs*, No. 1, 1890, p. 361.
5. Brigham, W. T., "Notes on the Eruption of the Hawaiian Volcanoes, 1868," Boston Society of Natural History, *Memoirs*, No. 1, 1868.
   Hitchcock, C. H., "The Hawaiian Earthquakes of 1868," *Bulletin of the Seismological Society of America*, Vol. 2, 1912, pp. 181–192.
   Wood, Harry O., "On the Earthquakes of 1868 in Hawaii," *Ibid.*, Vol. 4, 1914, pp. 169–203.
6. Davison, Charles, *The Japanese Earthquake of 1923*, (London: Thomas Murby and Co., 1931), pp. xii–128.
   Imamura, A., "A Diary on the Great (Japanese) Earthquake," *Bulletin of the Seismological Society of America*, Vol. 14, 1924, pp. 1–5.
   Jaggar, T. A., "The Yokohama-Tokyo Earthquake of September 1, 1923," *Ibid.*, Vol. 13, 1923, pp. 124–146.
7. Matsuyama, Montonori, "Notes on the Nature of the Kwanto Earthquake, Japan," Comptés rendus des séances de la deusiemé conférence réunié a Màdrid du 1 au 8 octobré 1924. Union Geodésiqué et Géophysique Internationalé, pp. 72–81; and in Series A of the publications by the same organization, *Travaux Scientifiques*, *Fascicule 2*, 1924, pp. 3–24.
   Suda, K., "The Great Japanese Earthquake of September 1, 1923," Kobe Imperial Marine Observatory, *Memoirs*, Vol. 1, 1924, pp. 137–239, 31 plates.
   Terada, T., "On the Vertical Displacement of the Sea Bottom in

Sagami Bay. Discovered after the Great Kwanto Earthquake of 1923," *Proceedings of the Imperial Academy* (Japan, 1928), Vol. 4, pp. 45–48.

Terada, T., and Miyabe, R., "On the Horizontal Displacement of the Primary Trigonometrical Points, Discovered after the Kwanto Earthquake," *Ibid.*, Vol. 4, 1928, pp. 49–52.

8. Jones, J. Claude, "The Pleasant Valley, Nevada, Earthquake of October 2, 1915," *Bulletin of the Seismological Society of America*, Vol. 5, Dec., 1915, pp. 190–205.

9. Tarr, Ralph S., and Martin, Lawrence, "The Earthquakes at Yakutat Bay, Alaska, in September, 1899," United States Geological Survey, *Professional Paper*, No. 69, 1921, pp. 1–135.

10. Fuller, Myron L., "The New Madrid Earthquake," United States Geological Survey, *Bulletins*, No. 494, 1912, pp. 101–119.

11. Dutton, Clarence Edward, "The Charleston Earthquake of August 31, 1886," United States Geological Survey, *Ninth Annual Report*, 1887–88, pp. 203–528.

12. Koto, B., "On the Cause of the Great Earthquake in Central Japan, 1891," Tokyo Imperial University, *Journal of the College of Science*, Vol. 5, Part I, pp. 295–353.

13. Yamasaki, N., and Tada, F., "The Oku-Tango Earthquake of 1927," Tokyo Imperial University, *Bulletin of the Earthquake Research Institute*, Vol. 4, 1928, pp. 159–178.

14. Hodgson, Ernest A., "Epicentral Time and Crustal Structure Determined for the Tango Earthquake, Japan, March 7, 1927," *Bulletin of the Seismological Society of America*, Vol. 22, 1932, pp. 270–287.

15. Tsuboi, C., "Investigation on the Deformation of the Earth's Crust in the Tango District Connected with the Tango Earthquake of 1927 (Part 1)," Tokyo Imperial University, *Bulletin of the Earthquake Research Institute*, Vol. 8, 1930, pp. 153–221.

16. Imamura, A., and Nasu, N., "On the Destructive Tango Earthquake of March 7, 1927; A Stereometrical Study of the Seismic Origin," *Proceedings of the Imperial Academy*, Japan, Vol. 3, 1927, pp. 227–231.

Nasu, N., "On the Crustal Block that Played an Important Role in the Destructive Tango Earthquake of 1927," *Ibid.*, Vol. 5, 1929, pp. 164–166.

17. Tsuya, H., "On the Geological Structure of the Tango Earthquake Region" (in Japanese with English résumé), Tokyo Imperial University, *Bulletin of the Earthquake Research Institute*, Vol. 4, 1928, pp. 139–158, and map.

18. Lyell, Sir Charles, *Principles of Geology or the Modern Changes of the Earth and Its Inhabitants* (New York, 1875), 12 Ed., pp. 82–89.

19. Ferrar, H. T., "The Murchison (N. Z.) Earthquake, 1929," *The Geological Magazine*, Vol. 67, 1930, pp. 132–134.

20. Davison, Charles, "The New Zealand Earthquake of February 3," *Nature*, Vol. 127, 1931, pp. 243–244.

21. Baker, W. E., "Remarks on the Allah Bund, and on the Drainage of the Eastern Part of the Scinde Basin, Etc.," *Transactions of the Bombay Geographical Society*, 1846, pp. 186–188.
Oldham, R. D., "A Note on the Allah-Bund in the North-West of the Rann of Kuchh," Geological Survey of India, *Memoirs*, Vol. 28, 1898, pp. 27–30.
22. Aguilera, J. G., "Estudio de los fenómenos seísmicios del 3 de mayo de 1887," Comisión Cientifica de, Sonora, Sección naturalista *Anales del Ministerio de Fomento*, Vol. 10, 1889, p. 5.
——— "The Sonora Earthquake of 1887," *Bulletin of the Seismological Society of America*, Vol. 10, 1920, pp. 31–44.
Goodfellow, G. E., "The Sonora Earthquake," *Science*, Vol. 11, 1888, pp. 162–166.
23. Omori, F., "Preliminary Note on the Formosa Earthquake of March 17, 1906," *Bulletin of the Imperial Earthquake Investigation Committee*, Vol. 1, 1907, pp. 53–69.
24. Baratta, N., "Catastrofe sismica Calabro-Messinese, 28 dicembre 1908," *Relazione alla Societa Geografica Italiana* (Rome, 1910), 426 pp.
Omori, F., "Preliminary Report on the Messina-Reggio Earthquake of December 28, 1908," *Bulletin of the Imperial Earthquake Investigation Committee* (Tokyo, 1909), Vol. 3, pp. 37–45.
25. Plantania, C., "Il maremoto dello stretto di Messina del 28 dicembre 1908," *Bullettino della Societa Sismologia Italiana*, Vol. 13, 1908–09, p. 369, Modena.
26. Novarese, "Il terremoto del 28 dicembre in Reggio, Calabria e Provincia," *Bulletino del Ufficio Geologico d'Italia* (Rome, 1910), Vol. 40, p. 424.
27. Middlemiss, C. S., "The Kangra Earthquake of 4th April 1905," *Memoirs of the Geological Survey of India*, Vol. 38, 1910, pp. 409 sq.
28. Middlemiss, C. S., *loc. cit.*, p. 334.
29. Omori, F., "Report on the Great Indian Earthquake of 1905. Part I. Seismograms," *Publications of the Earthquake Investigation Committee in Foreign Languages*, No. 23, 1907.
30. Oldham, R. D., "Report on the Great Earthquake of 12th June, 1897," Geological Survey of India, *Memoirs*, Vol. 29, 1899, 379 pp.
31. Griesbach, C. L., "Notes on the Earthquake in Baluchistan on the 20th December, 1892," *Records of the Geological Survey of India*, Vol. 26, Part 2, 1893, pp. 57–61.
32. Geological Survey of India, "The Bihar-Nepal Earthquake of 1934," *Memoirs*, Vol. 73, 1939, 391 pp.
33. Humboldt, A. von, *Cosmos*, translated from the German by E. C. Otte (London, 1849).
34. Wood, Harry O., "The Seismic Prelude to the 1914 Eruption of Mauna Loa," *Bulletin of the Seismological Society of America*, Vol. 5, 1915, pp. 39–51 — see map in Chap. 2, Fig. 42.
35. Omori, F., "The Usu-san Eruption and the Earthquake and Elevation

Phenomena," *Bulletin of the Imperial Earthquake Investigation Committee,* Vol. 5, 1911, pp. 1–38; 1913, pp. 101–107.

36. Omori, F., "The Eruptions and Earthquakes of the Asama-Yama," *Bulletin of the Imperial Earthquake Investigation Committee,* Vol. 6, 1912–14, pp. 1–257; Vol. 7, 1914–19, pp. 1–456.

37. Omori, F., "The Sakura-jima Eruptions and Earthquakes," *Bulletin of the Imperial Earthquake Investigation Committee,* Vol. 8, 1914–22, pp. 1–522.

———— "The Eruption of Sakura-jima," *Bulletin of the Seismological Society of America,* Vol. 5, 1915, pp. 71–95.

38. Omori, F., "The Sakura-jima Eruptions and Earthquakes. I. General Account," *Bulletin of the Imperial Earthquake Investigation Committee,* Vol. 8, 1914, pp. 33–34; also in same volume, 1920, pp. 393, 396.

———— "The Eruption of Sakura-jima, 1914," *Bulletin of the Seismological Society of America,* Vol. 5, 1915, pp. 71–95.

39. Wood, Harry O., "On the Earthquakes of 1868 in Hawaii," *Bulletin of the Seismological Society of America,* Vol. 4, 1914, pp. 169–203.

40. Wood, Harry O., "A Consideration of Recent Earthquakes Local to Hawaii and of the Seismological Problem They Indicate," Hawaiian Volcano Observatory, *Weekly Bulletin,* Vol. 3, 1915, pp. 53–65.

———— "The Tectonic Aspect of Volcanic Eruptions in Hawaii," *Special Publication of the Bernice P. Bishop Museum,* No. 7, 1921, pp. 346–353.

———— "Volcanic Earthquakes," chapter three of, *Physics of the Earth — VI — Seismology,* by Macelwane, *et al., Bulletin of the National Research Council No. 90* (Washington, 1933).

41. Fenner, C. N., "The Katmai Region, Alaska, and the Great Eruption of 1912," *Journal of Geology,* Vol. 28, 1920, pp. 569–606.

Griggs, R. F., "The Valley of Ten Thousand Smokes," *National Geographic Magazine,* Vol. 31, 1917, pp. 13–68.

Martin, G. C., "The Recent Eruption of Katmai Volcano in Alaska," *National Geographic Magazine,* Vol. 24, 1913, pp. 131–181.

Tams, E., "Erdbeben und Ausbruch des Katmai im Jahre 1912," *Zeitschrift für Vulkanologie,* Band 8, 1924, pp. 137–149 and Pl.

42. Tams, E., p. 146; *see* footnote 11.

43. Branca, W., "Über die Bedeutung der magmatischen Beben gegenüber den tektonischen," *Sitzungsberichte der königlichen Preussischen Akademie der Wissenschaften, physikalisch-mathematische Klasse,* Band 28, 1917.

44. Saderra Maso, Rev. M., S.J., "Recent Eruptions of the Bulusan Volcano, 1916 and 1918," *Bulletin of the Philippine Weather Bureau,* Jan., 1919, 4 pp.

———— "Recent Eruptions of the Bulusan Volcano, 1919–1922," *Ibid.,* June, 1922, 5 pp.

45. Saderro Maso, Rev. M., S.J., and Smith, W. D., "The Relation of

Seismic Disturbances in the Philippines to the Geologic Structure," *Philippine Journal of Science*, Vol. 8, Sec. A, 1913, pp. 199–233; and also in *Bulletin of the Seismological Society of America*, Vol. 3, 1913, pp. 151–186.

46. Hodgson, Ernest A., "Epicentral Time and Crustal Structure Determined for the Tango Earthquake, Japan, March 7, 1927," *Bulletin of the Seismological Society of America*, Vol. 22, 1932, pp. 270–287.

47. Turner, H. H., "On the Arrival of Earthquake Waves at the Antipodes, and on the Measurement of the Focal Depth of an Earthquake," *Monthly Notices of the Royal Astronomical Society, Geophysical Supplement*, Vol. 1, 1922, pp. 1–13.

———— "Shallow and Deep Earthquakes," *The Geophysical Magazine*, Vol. 2, 1929, pp. 179–187.

48. Oldham, R. D., "The Geological Interpretation of the Earth Movements Associated with the California Earthquake of April 18, 1906," *Quarterly Journal of the Geological Society of London*, Vol. 65, 1909, pp. 6–15, 5 fig.

———— "The Depth and Twofold Character of Earthquake Origins," *The Journal of Geology*, Vol. 34, 1926, pp. 385–398.

———— "Seismology," *Encyclopedia Brittanica*, 12 Ed., Vol. 32, 1922, pp. 390–391.

49. Pilgrim, L., "Die Berechnung der Laufzeiten eines Erdstosses mit Berücksichtigung der Herdtiefen, gestützt auf neuere Beobachtungen," *Gerlands Beiträge zur Geophysik*, Band 12, 1913, pp. 363–483.

50. Oldham, R. D., "The Geological Interpretation of the Earth Movements Associated with the California Earthquake of April 18, 1906," *Quarterly Journal of the Geological Society of London*, Vol. 65, 1909, pp. 1–16, 5 fig.

51. Walker, G. W., "Focal Depth and the Time Curve," *British Association Report*, 1917, p. 11.

———— "The Problem of Finite Focal Depth Revealed by the Seismometer," *Philosophical Transactions of the Royal Society of London*, Series A, Vol. 222, 1921, pp. 45–56.

52. Stechschulte, Rev. V. C., S.J., "Deep Focus Earthquakes," *Nature*, Vol. 128, 1931, pp. 673–674.

———— "The Japanese Earthquake of March 29, 1928, and the Problem of Depth of Focus," *Bulletin of the Seismological Society of America*, Vol. 22, 1932, pp. 81–137.

53. Scrase, F. J., "Deep Focus Earthquakes," *Nature*, Vol. 127, 1931, p. 486.

———— "The Reflected Waves From Deep Focus Earthquakes," *Proceedings of the Royal Society of London*, Series A, Vol. 132, 1931, pp. 213–235.

———— "The Characteristics of a Deep Focus Earthquake: A Study of the Disturbance of February 20, 1931," *Philosophical Trans-*

actions of the Royal Society of London, Series A, Vol. 231, 1933, pp. 207–234.

54. Wadati, K., "Shallow and Deep Earthquakes," *Geophysical Magazine,* Vol. 1, 1928, pp. 161–202; Vol. 2, 1930, pp. 1–36; Vol. 4, 1931, pp. 231–283.

55. Wadati, K., "Shallow and Deep Earthquakes," *Geophysical Magazine,* Vol. 1, 1928, pp. 162–202; Vol. 2, 1929, pp. 1–36; Vol. 4, 1931, pp. 231–283.

56. Stechschulte, Rev. V. C., S.J., "The Japanese Earthquake of March 29, 1928, and the Problem of Depth of Focus," *Bulletin of the Seismological Society of America,* Vol. 22, 1932, pp. 81–137.

57. Knopf, A., *A Geologic Reconnaissance of the Inyo Range and the Eastern Slope of the Sierra Nevada, California,* United States Geological Survey, *Professional Paper* (Washington, 1918), No. 110, 130 pp.

58. Lawson, A. C., "San Francisco," *Geologic Atlas of the United States* (Washington, D. C.: United States Geological Survey, 1915), Folio 193, structural map of the Tamalpais Quadrangle.

59. Leet, L. D., *Practical Seismology and Seismic Prospecting* (New York: D. Appleton-Century Co., 1938), p. 42.

60. Reid, H. F., "The Mechanics of Earthquakes. The Elastic Rebound Theory. Regional Strain," Chapter Nine of *Bulletin 90 of the National Research Council* (Washington, 1933); and the references there given.

61. Reid, *loc. cit.,* p. 88.

62. Reid, *loc. cit.,* pp. 88–90.

63. Heck, N. H., *Earthquake History of the United States,* 2 Ed., U. S. Coast and Geodetic Survey Special Publication, No. 149, 1928.

64. Townley, S. D., and Allen, M. W., "Descriptive Catalogue of the Earthquakes of the Pacific Coast of the United States 1769 to 1928," *Bulletin of the Seismological Society of America,* Vol. 29, No. 1, Jan., 1939.

65. Davison, C., *A History of British Earthquakes* (Cambridge: Cambridge University Press, 1924).

66. To illustrate how these two types of elastic wave motion arise, let us suppose a point P in Figure 252 to be inside of a large mass of homogeneous and perfectly elastic rock and let it be drawn over toward the right by an external force to the position P'. The portion of the rock to the right of P' will have been compressed while that to the left will have been stretched. Potential energy will have been stored in the rock by means of the volume changes. Also a straight line AB drawn through P perpendicular to PP' before the movement will have been distorted into a curved line similar to $A'P'B'$. Further potential energy will have been stored up in the rock mass through this distortion. Now let P' be released. The rock will not return at once to its previous position of equilibrium and remain there but will acquire a momentum which will carry it beyond P to some point P''. The portion of the rock

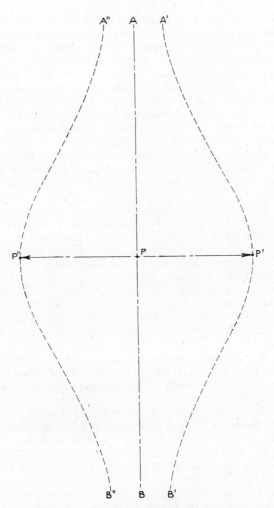

Fig. 252. Origin of longitudinal and
transverse waves.

on the right is now stretched and that on the left is compressed. While the portion of the rock at P' was passing through the position P all the potential energy of condensation and rarefaction had been changed into kinetic energy of translation parallel to $P'P''$ and the potential energy of distortion into kinetic energy of rotation about points on the original line AB above and below P. At P'' the energy is all potential again. The process will repeat itself until all the energy is radiated in the form of two independent types of waves, the one involving condensation and rarefaction, the other distortion or shear. Actually, the rocks of the earth's crust are not perfectly elastic, so that some of the elastic energy will be converted into heat thus gradually braking or damping the motion; but this will not modify the argument except to bring P'' closer to P.

67. Omori, F., "An Absolute Scale of Destructive Earthquakes," *Publications of the Earthquake Investigation Committee in Foreign Languages* (Tokyo, 1900), No. 4, pp. 137–141.

68. Cancani, A., "Sur l'emploi d'une double échelle sismique des intensités, empirique et absolue," *Verhandlungen der II. Seismologischen Konferenz zu Strassburg*, 1903.

69. McAdie, A., "President's Address," *Bulletin of the Seismological Society of America*, Vol. 5, 1915, pp.121–129.

70. Wood, H. O., "Destructive Effects and Intensity Scales," *Report of the California Earthquake Commission*, Vol. 1, Part 1, 1910, pp. 222–227.

71. Sieberg, A., "Ausführliche Skala zum Bestimmen der Erdbebenstärke, auf der Grundlage der Mercalli-Cancani-Skala," *Geologische physikalische und angewandte Erdbebenkunde* (Jena: Fischer, 1923), pp. 102–104.

72. Holden, E. S., "Remarks Upon Earthquake Intensity in San Francisco," *American Journal of Science*, Vol. 35, 1888, pp. 428–429.

73. Published in *Archives des Sciences Physique et Naturelles*, Vol. 11, 1884, pp. 148–149.

74. Published in the *Bolletino della Societa Sismologica Italiana*, Vol. 8, 1902, pp. 184–191.

75. Davison, Charles, "On Scales of Seismic Intensity and on the Construction and use of Isoseismal Lines," *Bulletin of the Seismological Society of America*, Vol. XI, 1921, pp. 95–129.

76. Wood, Harry O., and Neumann, Frank, "Modified Mercalli Intensity Scale of 1931," *Bulletin of the Seismological Society of America*, Vol. 21, 1931, pp. 277–283.

77. Sieberg, A., *Erdbebenkunde* (Jena: Fischer, 1923), pp. 102–104.

78. Dutton, C. E., "The Charleston Earthquake of August 31, 1886," United States Geological Survey, *Ninth Annual Report* (1887–88), pp. 203–528.

79. *Loc. cit.*, p. 128; also *Geological Magazine*, Vol. VIII, 1896, pp. 553–556.

80. Hicks, Henry, "On the Morte Slates and Associated Beds in North

Devon and West Somerset," *Quarterly Journal of the Geological Society,* Vol. 52, 1896, pp. 254–272; also Vol. 53, 1897, pp. 438–462.

81. Evans, J. W., and Pocock, R. W., *Geological Magazine,* Vol. 24, 1912, pp. 113–115.

82. Davison, Charles, "On Earthquake Sounds," *Philosophical Magazine,* Vol. 49, 1900, pp. 31–70.
———— "The Sound Phenomena of British Earthquakes," *Gerlands Beiträge zur Geophysik,* Vol. 12,.1913, pp. 485–527.

83. Davison, Charles, *A Manual of Seismology* (Cambridge: Cambridge University Press, 1921), pp. 56–68.

84. Freeman, J. R., *Earthquake Damage and Earthquake Insurance* (New York: McGraw-Hill, 1932).

85. Freeman, J. R., "Engineering Data Needed on Earthquake Motion for Use in the Design of Earthquake-Resisting Structures," *Bulletin Seismological Society of America,* Vol. 20, 1930, pp. 67–87.

86. United States Coast and Geodetic Survey, *Special Publication,* No. 201, and Serials No. 579, 593, 600, 610, 619, 629, 637.

87. Hall, Elmer E., "Vibrations of Buildings due to Street Traffic," *Engineering News,* Vol. 68, 1912, p. 198. *See also* Derleth, C., "Vibration of the Sather Tower," *Bulletin Imperial Earthquake Investigation Committee of Japan,* Vol. 9, 1921, pp. 100–107.

88. Byerly, P., Hester, J., and Marshall, K., "The Natural Periods of Vibration of Some Tall Buildings in San Francisco," *Bulletin Seismological Society of America,* Vol. 21, 1931, pp. 268–276.

89. Anon., "Vibrations in Saint Paul's due to Traffic," and "Vibrations in the Clock Tower at Westminster," *Engineering,* Vol. 97, p. 881, and Vol. 98, pp. 27–31, 74–77.

90. Carder, D. S., "Vibration Observations," *Earthquake Investigations in California,* United States Coast and Geodetic Survey, *Special Publication,* No. 201, Chap. 5, pp. 49–106.

91. Ruge, A. C., "A Machine for Reproducing Earthquake Motions Direct From a Shadowgraph of the Earthquake," *Bulletin of the Seismological Society of America,* Vol. 26, 1936, pp. 201–205.

92. Jacobsen, L. S., "Experimental Study of the Dynamic Behavior of Models of Timber Walls Subjected to an Impulsive Horizontal Ground Vibration," *Bulletin of the Seismological Society of America,* Vol. 20, 1930, pp. 115–146.

93. Bierer, R. W., and Parker, T. B., "An Experimental Investigation of the Resistance of Masonry to Vibration with Special Reference to the Effect of Earthquake Waves," *Bulletin of the Seismological Society of America,* Vol. 1, 1911, pp. 107–108.

94. Alvarez, A. C., "Wall Bracing in Timber Frame Buildings," *Bulletin of the Seismological Society of America,* Vol. 15, 1925, pp. 159–167.

95. Köhler, R., "Die Resonanzmethode als Hilfsmittel bei seismischen Untersuchungen," *Zeitschrift für Geophysik,* Vol. 8, 1932, pp. 461–467.

96. Patterson, W. D., "Determination of Ground Periods," *Bulletin of the Seismological Society of America,* Vol. 30, 1940, pp. 129–138.

97. Thoenen, J. R., and Windes, S. L., "Seismic Effects of Quarry Blasting," United States Bureau of Mines, *Bulletin 442,* 1942.

98. Symposium (Philip P. Bucky, presiding), "Rock Bursts," A.I.M.M.E., *Technical Paper 1468,* 56 pp.

99. Hodgson, E. A., "Velocity of Elastic Waves and Structure of the Crust in the Vicinity of Ottawa, Canada," *Bulletin of the Seismological Society of America,* Vol. 32, 1942, pp. 249–255, and mimeographed report, August 13, 1943.

100. Hodgson, E. A., "Rockburst Research at Lake Shore Mines," *Miner and Mine,* Vol. 1, 1943, pp. 4–5, 15; also mimeographed reports.

101. Obert, Leonard A., "Use of Subaudible Noises for Prediction of Rock Bursts," United States Bureau of Mines *Reports of Investigations,* No. 3555, 1941; and No. 3654, 1942.

102. Hodgson, E. A., "Recent Developments in Rockburst Research at Lake Shore Mines," Canadian Institute of Mining and Metallurgy, *Transactions,* Vol. 46, 1943, pp. 313–324; also mimeographed reports.

103. Griggs, David T., "Deformation of Rocks under High Confining Pressures," *Journal of Geology,* Vol. 44, 1936, pp. 541–577.

104. Bridgman, P. W., *The Physics of High Pressure* (New York: Macmillan, 1931).
——— "Shearing Phenomena at High Pressure of Possible Importance for Geology," *Journal of Geology,* Vol. 44, 1936, pp. 653–669.
——— "The High-Pressure Behavior of Miscellaneous Minerals," *American Journal of Science,* Vol. 51, 1940, pp. 1001–1034.

105. Allen, V. T., *This Earth of Ours,* Science and Culture Series (Milwaukee: The Bruce Publishing Co., 1939), 364 pp.

APPENDIX C

GLOSSARY

ACCELEROGRAPH. A seismograph whose natural period of free vibration is very much shorter than that of the waves it is intended to record.

ALLUVIUM. Unconsolidated stream deposits of sand and mud.

AMPLIFIER. An electronic network designed to increase enormously the output of an electric system.

ANGLE OF INCIDENCE. Angle between an incident ray and the normal to the surface on which it impinges.

ANHYDRITE. Anhydrous calcium sulphate.

ANTICENTER. The point at the antipodes of the epicenter.

ANTICLINE. Upward bend in folded strata.

ARGILLITE. Hard, brittle shale without cleavage.

AXIS OF ROTATION. Line of stationary points in a rotating body.

BASALT. A dark colored, fine-grained, basic igneous rock.

BODY WAVE. An elastic wave in the interior of a body, as distinguished from a surface wave or boundary wave.

CAPACITY. The electric charge required to raise a condenser to unit potential.

CONDENSER. An electric instrument consisting of insulation between two unconnected conductors.

CONGLOMERATE. A rock composed of rounded pebbles of various sizes intermingled with a finer material that acts as a cement.

COUPLE. A pair of equal torques working together to produce rotation in the same direction around a common axis.

CRATER. Hollow in the top of a volcano.

CRITICAL ANGLE. Angle of incidence at which "total" internal reflection occurs and the refracted ray becomes theoretically parallel to the reflecting and refracting surface.

DELTA. Alluvial deposit at the mouth of a river, usually triangular in shape.

DENSITY. Mass per unit volume.

DETRITUS. Loose fragments of rock.

DRAG. Backward folding of rock strata by friction during faulting.

EARTHQUAKE. A shaking of the earth's surface caused by a passing disturbance of the elastic equilibrium of the rock masses below.

EARTHQUAKE HEARTH. *See* Focus.

EARTHQUAKE WAVE. An elastic vibration set up by an earthquake and propagated through or around the earth.

ELASTIC LIMIT. Maximum strain to which an elastic body may be subjected without permanent set.

ELASTIC REBOUND. The fling or spring back of an elastic body when a deforming force is suddenly removed.

ELECTROMECHANICAL TRANSDUCER. Arrangement for changing mechanical energy into electrical energy or vice versa.

EPEIROGENIC. Continent forming.

EPICENTER. The geographical location of the point on the surface of the earth that is vertically above the focus.

FAULT. A plane or zone of fracture on the two walls of which the rocks have been relatively displaced.

FAULT BRECCIA. Rock broken into angular fragments by relative movements in a fault zone.

FAULT GOUGE. Finely ground rock between the walls of a fault.

FAULTING. Fracture and relative displacement of rocks overstrained beyond their ultimate strength.

FAULT SCARP. Cliff along a fault produced by relative vertical displacement.

FELDSPAR. Any one of a group of silicates of aluminum and of potassium (orthoclase), or sodium (albite), or calcium (anorthite), and solid solutions of any two, such as the soda-lime feldspar (plagioclase).

FILTER. An arrangement for emphasizing certain frequencies and suppressing others.

FIORD. A long narrow arm of the sea with high rocky banks.

FOCUS. The source or origin of the first earthquake waves that are strong enough to be recorded by seismographs. Also called *hypocenter* and *hearth*.

FOSSIL. Any record of past life whether it is the whole or a part of an organism or any record of its presence left in the rocks.

FREQUENCY. The number of vibrations per second. Reciprocal of the period.

GEOPHONE. A prospecting seismometer.

GRABEN. A trench or trough or valley formed by dropping the floor between two faults.

GRANITE. A completely crystalline acidic igneous rock containing quartz and orthoclase.

GRAPHITE. A form of carbon which serves as a lubricant.

GRAVITY. The mechanical force with which any two bodies attract each other. Specifically the earth's attraction; the corresponding acceleration, usually given the symbol g.

GRAVITY ANOMALY. A value of g which departs from the theoretically expected value at the point.

HOOKE'S LAW.   *Ut tensio, sic vis.* Stress is proportional to strain.
HYDROSTATIC EQUILIBRIUM.   Equal pressure in all directions at equal
   depths.
HYPOCENTER.   *See* Focus.

IGNEOUS ROCK.   A rock that has solidified from a hot, molten condition.
INERTIA.   A property of all matter which tends to keep a body in the
   same state of rest or of motion.
ISACOUSTIC LINE.   A closed curve through all places at which the same
   percentage of people heard the earthquake sounds.
ISOSEISMAL LINE OR ISOSEIST.   A closed curve drawn through points of
   equal earthquake intensity.
ISOSTASY.   A condition of quasi-hydrostatic balance between adjacent
   segments of the earth's crust.

LANDSLIDE.   Slipping of a mass of land from a higher to a lower level.
LAVA.   Molten or solidified rock from a volcano.
LIMESTONE.   A sedimentary rock composed largely of calcium carbonate.

MAGMA.   The molten mass from which igneous rocks are formed by differ-
   entiation and cooling.
MAGNIFICATION.   Ratio of the recorded response of a seismograph to the
   corresponding quantity in the actual motion of the ground, whether
   displacements, or velocities, or accelerations.
MASS.   Quantity of matter present in a body. Ratio of force to acceleration produced.
MATRIX.   A rock mass in which a crystal or fossil, or other object is
   embedded.
METAMORPHIC ROCK.   Rocks profoundly altered by pressure, heat, moisture, etc., usually at considerable depth.
MILLEPORES.   Coral-like animals living in tiny cavities on the surface of
   a structure they deposit from sea water.
MINERAL.   A naturally occurring inorganic substance with definite physical characteristics and chemical composition.

NORMAL FAULT.   A fault with downthrow on the upper, or hanging wall
   side (see Fig. 250).
NUNATAK.   A small peak or island of rock projecting upward through a
   glacier.

OCEAN DEEP.   Trough-like depression in the sea bed.
OROGENIC.   Mountain building.
ORTHOCLASE.   A feldspar composed of potassium, aluminum, and silica.
OVERSTRAIN.   Strain beyond the elastic limit.

PENEPLAIN.   A low, rolling land surface approaching a plain above which
   erosion remnants project as monadnocks. The end product of the erosion
   cycle.
PERIOD OF VIBRATION.   The time required for one complete to-and-fro
   movement of a given point in a vibrating body.

PHASE. (1) Fraction of a complete vibration. (2) Fresh onset of waves in a seismogram.

PLANETOID. One of the several hundred small planets revolving around the sun between the orbits of Mars and Jupiter.

P-WAVE. A push-and-pull or longitudinal earthquake wave.

QUARTZ. A hard mineral composed of silicon dioxide.

QUARTZITE. A metamorphic rock composed of quartz grains cemented by silica.

QUARTZ-MONZONITE. A light-colored crystalline igneous rock related to granite.

RAY. Perpendicular to a wave front.

RESISTANCE. In electrical theory, the ratio of the potential difference to the current produced. Ohms equal volts divided by amperes.

RESONANCE. Equality between the tempo of the forcing motion and the natural frequency of the body acted upon.

REVERSE FAULT. A fault with downthrow on the lower, or foot, wall side (see Fig. 250). A thrust fault.

RHYOLITE. A light-colored, fine-grained igneous rock of the same composition as granite.

RIFT. A valley eroded in the soft gouge and breccia of a fault zone between valley walls of a firmer rock.

ROCK BURST, or MINE BURST. Failure with explosive suddenness and violence of large blocks of rock under compression in a mine, or the explosive spalling of walls of mine openings, or a sudden slip on a fault in the worked territory.

ROCK SLIDE. Slipping down of a mass of rock.

ROTATION. Motion of a rigid body in which, at any instant, there exists a line of points that are relatively stationary while all the other points in the body move in circular paths around this *axis*.

SALT DOME. The dome-like structure over a salt plug.

SAND BLOW. Sand ejected with water from a fissure during an earthquake and spread out over the soil.

SAND CRATER. A hole surrounded by a ring of sand ejected with water during an earthquake.

SANDSTONE. A rock composed of grains of quartz held together by a cement.

SCHIST. A metamorphic rock in which the minerals are arranged in thin layers which split apart easily.

SEA QUAKE. An earthquake felt on board a ship at sea.

SEDIMENTARY ROCKS. Made-over rocks, especially water-laid deposits.

SEISMOGRAPH. An instrument for quantitative recording of ground vibration.

SEISMOLOGY. A branch of the science of geophysics dealing with the nature, causes, and effects of earthquakes; with elastic waves in the earth and their use in the study of earth structure and in prospecting;

and with the engineering problems that arise from earthquakes, both natural and artificial.

SHALE. Compacted mud or clay that possesses a laminated or fissile structure.

SIMPLE HARMONIC MOTION. Such a real motion as uniform motion in circle would appear to be if viewed from a distance with the eye in the same plane as the circle.

SLATE. A homogeneous metamorphosed clay or shale characterized by a remarkable cleavage which causes it to split readily into broad thin sheets.

SLIVER. A detached, relatively thin sheet of rock separated from the parent mass by faulting.

SLUMP. Slipping of soil down a slight incline.

STRAIN. Deformation of an elastic body within the elastic limit of the material.

STRATA. Layers of sedimentary rocks.

STRESS. The internal restoring forces in an elastic body that oppose the action of a deforming force and tend to restore the body to its original size and shape when that force is removed.

S-WAVE. An earthquake body wave of the shear or transverse type.

SYNCLINE. Downward bend in folded strata.

TECTONIC. Structural. Related to folding and faulting.

TORQUE. A force applied with a lever arm to produce rotation.

TRAJECTORY. Path described by a moving object, such as a projectile, or a parcel of energy in a wave front.

TRANSLATION. Motion in which all points of a body move along parallel straight lines.

TRIANGULATION. A method of precise surveying which starts with the exact measurement of a base line and then builds a system of triangles upon it.

WARPING. Gentle flexure of the surface of the ground without visible faulting.

WAVE LENGTH. The distance between two contiguous crests, or between two successive troughs, or between any particle and the next particle along a wave profile that is in the same phase.

INDEX